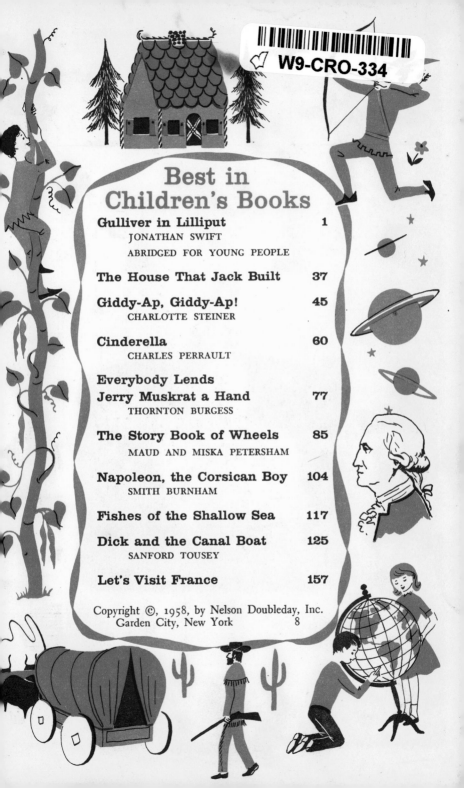

Best in Children's Books

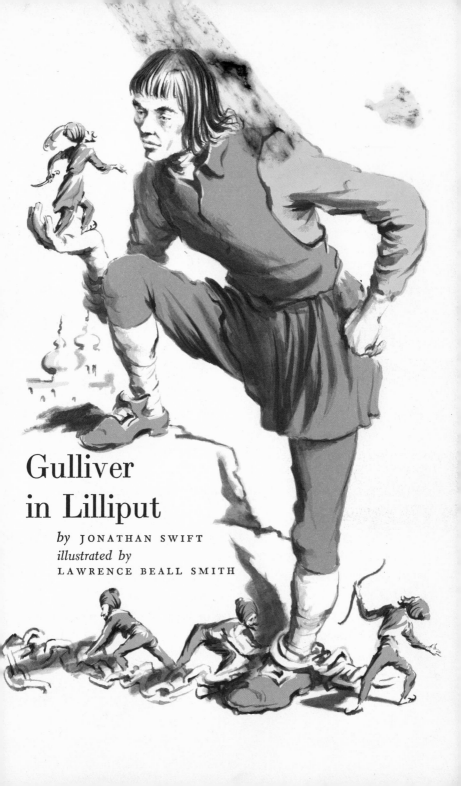

Gulliver
in Lilliput

by JONATHAN SWIFT
illustrated by
LAWRENCE BEALL SMITH

1

My father had a small estate in Nottinghamshire, and I was the third of four sons. He sent me to Cambridge at the age of fourteen, and after studying three years I was bound apprentice to Mr. Bates, a famous surgeon in London. There, as my father now and then sent me small sums of money, I spent them in learning navigation and other arts useful to those who travel, as I always believed it would be some time or other my fortune to do.

Text of "A Voyage to Lilliput," adapted from Jonathan Swift's *Gulliver's Travels* in Andrew Lang's *Blue Fairy Book*, 1889, 1929, by Longmans, Green and Co., Inc.

Three years after leaving him my good master, Mr. Bates, recommended me as ship's surgeon to the *Swallow*, on which I voyaged three years. When I came back I settled in London, and having taken part of a small house, I married Miss Mary Burton, daughter of Mr. Edmund Burton, hosier.

But my good master Bates died two years after, and as I had few friends my business began to fail, and I determined to go again to sea. After several voyages, I accepted an offer from Captain W. Prichard, master of the *Antelope*, who was making a voyage to the South Sea. We set sail from Bristol on May 4, 1699, and our voyage at first was very prosperous.

But in our passage to the East Indies we were driven by a violent storm to the northwest of Van Diemen's Land. Twelve of our crew died from hard labor and bad food, and the rest were in a very weak condition. On November 5, the weather being very hazy, the seamen spied a rock within one hundred and twenty yards of the ship; but the wind was so strong that we were driven straight upon it, and immediately split. Six of the crew, of whom I was one, letting down the boat, got clear of the ship, and we rowed about three leagues, till we could row no longer. We therefore trusted ourselves to the mercy of the waves, and in about an hour the boat was upset by a sudden squall. What became of my companions in the boat, or those who escaped on the rock or were left in the vessel, I cannot tell, but I conclude they were all lost. For my part, I swam as fortune directed me and was pushed forward by wind and tide; but when I was able to struggle no longer I found myself within my depth. By this time the storm was much abated.

I reached the shore at last, about eight o'clock in the evening, and advanced nearly half a mile inland, but could not discover any sign of inhabitants. I was extremely tired, and with the heat of the weather I found myself much inclined to sleep. I lay down on the grass, which was very short and soft, and slept sounder than ever I did in my life for about nine hours. When I woke it was just daylight. I attempted to rise, but could not; for as I happened to be lying on my back, I found my arms and legs were fastened on each side to the ground, and my hair, which was long and thick, tied down in the same manner. I could only look upward. The sun began to grow hot, and the light hurt my eyes. I heard a confused noise about me, but could see nothing except the sky.

In a little time I felt something alive moving on my left leg, which, advancing gently over my breast, came almost up to my chin. Bending my eyes downward, I then perceived it to be a human creature, not six inches high, with a bow and arrow in his hands and a quiver at his back. In the meantime, I felt at least forty more following the first. I was in the utmost astonishment, and roared so loud that they all ran back in a fright; and some of them were hurt with the falls they got by leaping from my sides upon the ground. However, they soon returned, and one of them, who ventured so far as to get a full sight of my face, lifted up his hands in admiration. I lay all this while in great uneasiness; but at length, struggling to get loose, I succeeded in breaking the strings that fastened my left arm to the ground, and at the same time, with a violent pull that gave me extreme pain, I loosened a little the strings

that tied down my hair, so that I was just able to turn my head about two inches.

But the creatures ran off a second time before I could seize them, whereupon there was a great shout, and in an instant I felt over a hundred arrows discharged on my left hand, which pricked me like so many needles. Moreover, they shot another flight into the air, of which some fell on my face, which I immediately covered with my left hand. When this shower of arrows was over, I groaned with grief and pain, and as I strove again to get loose, they discharged another flight of arrows, larger than the first, and some of them tried to stab me with their spears; but by good luck I had on a leather jacket, which they could not pierce. By this time I thought it most prudent to lie still till night, when, my left hand being already loose, I could easily free myself; and as for the inhabitants, I thought I might be a match for the greatest army they could bring against me if they were all of the same size as him I saw.

When the people observed that I was quiet they discharged no more arrows, but by the noise I knew that their number was increased, and about four yards from me, for more than an hour, there was a knocking, like people at work. Then, turning my head that way as well as the pegs and strings would let me, I saw a stage set up, about a foot and a half from the ground, with two or three ladders to mount it. From this, one of them, who seemed to be a person of quality, made me a long speech, of which I could not understand a word, though I could tell from his manner that he sometimes threatened me and sometimes spoke with pity and kindness. I answered in few words, but in the most submissive manner, and being almost famished with hunger, I could not help showing my impatience by putting my finger frequently to my mouth, to signify that I wanted food.

He understood me very well, and descending from the stage commanded that several ladders should be set against my sides, on which more than a hundred of the inhabitants mounted and walked toward my mouth with baskets full of food, which had been sent by the king's orders when he first received tidings of me. There were legs and shoulders like mutton, but smaller than the wings of a lark. I ate them two or three at a mouthful and took three loaves at a time. They supplied me as fast as they could, with a thousand marks of wonder at my appetite. I then made a sign that I wanted something to drink. They guessed that a small quantity would not suffice me, and being a most ingenious people, they slung up one of their largest hogsheads, then rolled it toward my hand, and beat out the top. I drank it off at a draught, which I might well do, for it did not hold half a pint. They brought me a second hogshead, which I drank. I made signs for more; but they had none to give me. However, I could not wonder enough at the daring of these tiny mortals who ventured to mount and walk upon my body, while one of my hands was free, without trembling at the very sight of so huge a creature as I must have seemed to them.

After some time there appeared before me a person of high rank from his imperial majesty. His excellency, having mounted my right leg, advanced to my face with about a dozen of his retinue, and spoke about ten minutes, often

9

pointing forward, which, as I afterward found, was toward the capital city, about half a mile distant, whither it was commanded by his majesty that I should be conveyed. I made a sign with my hand that was loose, putting it to the other (but over his excellency's head, for fear of hurting him or his train), to show that I desired my liberty. He seemed to understand me well enough, for he shook his head, though he made other signs to let me know that I should have meat and drink enough and very good treatment.

Then I once more thought of attempting to escape, but when I felt the smart of their arrows on my face and hands, which were all in blisters, and observed likewise that the number of my enemies increased, I gave tokens to let them know that they might do with me what they pleased. Then they daubed my face and hands with a sweet-smelling ointment, which in a few minutes removed all the smart of the arrows. The relief from pain and hunger made me drowsy, and presently I fell asleep. I slept about eight hours, as I was told afterward; and it was no wonder, for the physicians, by the emperor's order, had mingled a sleeping-draught in the hogshead of wine.

It seems that when I was discovered sleeping on the ground after my landing the emperor had early notice of it, and determined that I should be tied in the manner I have related (which was done in the night while I slept), that plenty of meat and drink should be sent to me, and a machine prepared to carry me to the capital city. Five hundred carpenters and engineers were immediately set to work to prepare the engine. It was a frame of wood, raised three inches from the ground, about seven feet long and four wide, moving upon twenty-two wheels. But the difficulty was to place me on it. Eighty poles were erected for this purpose, and very strong cords fastened to bandages which the workmen tied round my neck, hands, body, and legs. Nine hundred of the strongest men were employed to draw up these cords by pulleys fastened on the poles, and in less than three hours I was raised and slung into the engine and there tied fast. Fifteen hundred of the emperor's largest horses, each about four inches and a half high, were then employed to draw me toward the capital. But while all this was done I still lay in a deep sleep, and I did not wake till four hours after we began our journey.

The emperor and all his court came out to meet us when we reached the capital, but his great officials would not suffer his majesty to risk his person by mounting on my body. Where the carriage stopped there stood an ancient temple, supposed to be the largest in the whole kingdom, and here it was determined that I should lodge. Near the great gate, through which I could easily creep, they fixed ninety-one chains like those which hang to a lady's watch, which were locked to my left leg with thirty-six padlocks; and when the workmen found it was impossible for me to break loose, they cut all the strings that bound me. Then I rose up, feeling as melancholy as ever I did in my life. But the noise and astonishment of the people on seeing me rise and walk were inexpressible. The chains that held my left leg were about two yards long, and gave me not only freedom to walk backward and forward in a semicircle, but to creep in and lie at full length inside the temple.

2

The emperor, advancing toward me from among his courtiers, all most magnificently clad, surveyed me with great admiration, but kept beyond the length of my chain. He was graceful, majestic and taller by about the breadth of my nail than any of his court, which alone was enough to strike awe into the beholders. The better to behold him I lay down on my side, so that my face was level with his, and he stood three yards off. However, I have had him since many times in my hand, and therefore cannot be deceived. His dress was very simple, but he wore a light helmet of gold adorned with jewels and a plume. He held his sword in his hand, to defend himself if I should break loose; it was almost three inches long, and the hilt was of gold, enriched with diamonds. His voice was shrill, but very clear. His imperial majesty spoke often to me, and I answered; but neither of us could understand a word.

After about two hours the court retired, and I was left with a strong guard to keep away the crowd, some of whom had the impudence to shoot their arrows at me as I sat by the door of my house. But the colonel ordered six of them to be seized and delivered bound into my hands. I put five of them into my coat pocket; and as to the sixth, I made a face as if I would eat him alive. The poor man screamed terribly, and the colonel and his officers were much distressed, especially when they saw me take out my penknife. But I soon set them at ease, for, cutting the strings he was bound with, I put him gently on the ground, and away he ran. I treated the rest in the same manner, taking them one by one out of my pocket; and I saw that both the soldiers and people were highly delighted at this mark of my kindness.

Toward night I got with some difficulty into my house, where I lay on the ground, as I had to do for a fortnight, till a bed was prepared for me out of six hundred beds of the ordinary measure.

Six hundred servants were appointed to me and three hundred tailors made me a suit of clothes. Moreover, six of his majesty's greatest scholars were employed to teach me their language, so that soon I was able to converse after a fashion with the emperor, who often honored me with his visits. The first words I learned were to desire that he would please to give me my liberty, which I every day repeated on my knees; but he answered that this must be a work of time, and that first I must swear a peace with him and his kingdom. He told me also that by the laws of the nation I must be searched by two of the officers, and that as this could not be done without my help, he trusted them in my hands, and whatever they took from me should be returned when I left the country. I took up the two officers and put them into my coat pockets. These gentlemen, having pen, ink, and paper about them, made an exact list of everything they saw, which I afterward translated into English and which ran as follows:

"In the right coat pocket of the great man-mountain we found only one great piece of coarse cloth, large enough to cover the carpet of your majesty's chief room of state. In the left pocket we saw a huge silver chest, with a silver cover, which we could not lift. We desired that it should be opened, and one of us stepping into it found himself up to the mid-leg in a sort of dust, some of which flying into our faces sent us both into a fit of sneezing. In his right waistcoat pocket we found a number of white thin substances, folded one over another, about the size of three men, tied with a strong cable, and marked with black figures, which we humbly conceive to be writings. In the left there was a sort of engine, from the back of which extended twenty long poles, with which we conjecture the man-mountain combs his head. In the smaller pocket on the right side were several round flat pieces of white and red metal, of different sizes. Some of the white, which appeared to be silver, were so large and heavy that my comrades and I could hardly lift them. From another pocket hung a huge silver chain, with a wonderful kind of engine fastened to it, a globe half silver and half of some transparent metal; for on the transparent side we saw certain strange figures, and thought we could touch them till we found our fingers stopped by the shining substance. This engine made an incessant noise, like a water mill, and we conjecture it is either some unknown animal or the god he worships, but probably the latter, for he has told us that he seldom did anything without consulting it. This is a list of what we found about the body of the man-mountain, who treated us with great civility."

I had one private pocket which escaped their search, containing a pair of spectacles and a small spy-glass, which, being of no consequence to the emperor, I did not think myself bound in honor to reveal.

3

My gentleness and good behavior so gained favor with the emperor and his court, and, indeed, with the people in general, that I began to hope of getting my liberty in a short time. The natives came by degrees to be less fearful of danger from me. I would sometimes lie down and let five or six of them dance on my hand, and at last the boys and girls ventured to come and play at hide-and-seek in my hair.

The horses of the army and of the royal stables were no longer shy, having been daily led before me; and one of the emperor's huntsmen, on a large courser, jumped over my foot, shoe and all, which was indeed a prodigious leap. I amused the emperor one day in a very extraordinary manner. I took nine sticks and fixed them firmly in the ground in a square. Then I took four other sticks and tied them parallel at each corner, about two feet from the ground. I fastened my handkerchief to the nine sticks that stood erect and extended it on all sides till it was as tight as the top of a drum; and I desired the emperor to let a troop of his best horses, twenty-four in number, come and exercise upon this plain. His majesty approved of the proposal. I took them up one by one, with the proper officers to exercise them. As soon as they got into order they divided into two parties, discharged blunt arrows, drew their swords, fled and pursued, and, in short, showed the best military discipline I ever beheld. The parallel sticks secured them and their horses from falling off the stage, and the emperor was so much delighted that he ordered this entertainment to be repeated several days and persuaded the empress herself to let me hold her in her chair within two yards of the stage, whence she could view the whole performance. Fortunately no accident happened, only once a fiery horse, pawing with his hoof, struck a hole in my handkerchief and overthrew his rider and himself. But I immediately relieved them both, and covering the hole with one hand, I set down the troop with the other as I had taken them up. The horse that fell was strained in the shoulder, but the rider was not hurt, and I repaired my handkerchief as well as I could. However, I would not trust to the strength of it any more in such dangerous enterprises.

I had sent so many petitions for my liberty that his majesty at length mentioned the matter in a full council, where it was opposed by none except Skyresh Bolgolam, admiral of the realm, who was pleased without any provocation to be my mortal enemy. He agreed at length, though he succeeded in himself drawing up the conditions on which I should be set free. After they were read, I was requested to swear to perform them in the method prescribed by their laws, which was to hold my right foot in my left hand, to place the middle finger of my right hand on the crown of my head, and my thumb on the top of my right ear. But I have made a translation of the conditions, which I here offer to the public:

"Golbaste Momarem Evlame Gurdile Shefin Mully Ully Gue, Most Mighty Emperor of Lilliput, delight and terror of the universe, whose dominions extend to the ends of the globe, monarch of all monarchs, taller than the sons of men, whose feet press down to the center and whose head strikes against the sun, at whose nod the princes of the earth shake their knees, pleasant as the spring, comfortable as the summer, fruitful as autumn, dreadful as winter: his most sublime majesty proposeth to the man-mountain, lately arrived at our celestial dominions, the following articles, which by a solemn oath he shall be obliged to perform:

"First. The man-mountain shall not depart from our dominions without our license under the great seal.

"Second. He shall not presume to come into our metropolis without our express order, at which time the inhabitants shall have two hours' warning to keep within doors.

"Third. The said man-mountain shall confine his walks to our principal highroads, and not offer to walk or lie down in a meadow or field of corn.

"Fourth. As he walks the said road, he shall take the utmost care not to trample upon the bodies of any of our loving subjects, their horses or carriages, nor take any of our subjects into his hands without their own consent.

"Fifth. If an express requires extraordinary speed, the man-mountain shall be obliged to carry in his pocket the messenger and horse a six days' journey, and return the said messenger (if so required) safe to our imperial presence.

"Sixth. He shall be our ally against our enemies in the island of Blefuscu and do his utmost to destroy their fleet, which is now preparing to invade us.

"Lastly. Upon his solemn oath to observe all the above articles, the said man-mountain shall have a daily allowance of meat and drink sufficient for the support of seventeen hundred and twenty-four of our subjects, with free access to our royal person and other marks of our favor.

"Given at our palace of Belfaborac, the twelfth day of the ninety-first moon of our reign."

I swore to these articles with great cheerfulness, whereupon my chains were immediately unlocked and I was at full liberty.

One morning, about a fortnight after I had obtained my freedom, Reldresal, the emperor's secretary for private affairs, came to my house, attended only by one servant. He ordered his coach to wait at a distance and desired that I would give him an hour's audience. I offered to lie down that he might the more conveniently reach my ear, but he chose rather to let me hold him in my hand during our conversation. He began with compliments on my liberty, but he added that, save for the present state of things at court, perhaps I might not have obtained it so soon.

"For," he said, "however flourishing we may seem to foreigners, we are in danger of an invasion from the island

of Blefuscu, which is the other great empire of the universe, almost as large and as powerful as this of his majesty. For as to what we have heard you say, that there are other kingdoms in the world, inhabited by human creatures as large as yourself, our philosophers are very doubtful, and rather conjecture that you dropped from the moon or one of the stars, because a hundred mortals of your size would soon destroy all the fruit and cattle of his majesty's dominions. Besides, our histories of six thousand moons make no mention of any other regions than the two mighty empires of Lilliput and Blefuscu, which, as I was going to tell you, are engaged in a most obstinate war, which began in the following manner: It is allowed on all hands that the primitive way of breaking eggs was upon the larger end; but his present majesty's grandfather, while he was a boy, going to eat an egg, and breaking it according to the ancient practice, happened to cut one of his fingers. Whereupon the emperor, his father, made a law commanding all his subjects to break the smaller end of their eggs. The people so highly resented this law that there have been six rebellions raised on that account, wherein one emperor lost his life and another his crown. It is calculated that eleven hundred persons have at different times suffered death rather than break their eggs at the smaller end. But these rebels, the Bigendians, have found so much encouragement at the Emperor of Blefuscu's court, to which they always fled for refuge, that a bloody war, as I said, has been carried on between the two empires for thirty-six moons; and now the Blefuscudians have equipped a large fleet and are preparing to descend upon us. Therefore his imperial majesty, placing great confidence in your valor and strength, has commanded me to set the case before you."

I desired the secretary to present my humble duty to the emperor, and to let him know that I was ready, at the risk of my life, to defend him against all invaders.

4

It was not long before I communicated to his majesty the plan I formed for seizing the enemy's whole fleet. The empire of Blefuscu is an island parted from Lilliput only by a channel eight hundred yards wide. I consulted the most experienced seamen on the depth of the channel, and they told me that in the middle, at high water, it was seventy glumgluffs (about six feet of European measure). I walked toward the coast, where, lying down behind a hillock, I took out my spyglass and viewed the enemy's fleet at anchor—about fifty men-of-war and other vessels. I then came back to my house and gave orders for a great quantity of the strongest cables and bars of iron. The cable was about as thick as pack-thread and the bars of the length and size of a knitting-needle. I trebled the cable to make it stronger, and for the same reason twisted three of the

iron bars together, bending the ends into a hook.

Having thus fixed fifty hooks to as many cables, I went back to the coast, and taking off my coat, shoes, and stockings, walked into the sea in my leather jacket about half an hour before high water. I waded with what haste I could, swimming in the middle about thirty yards, till I felt ground, and thus arrived at the fleet in less than half an hour. The enemy were so frightened when they saw me that they leaped out of their ships and swam ashore, where there could not be fewer than thirty thousand. Then, fastening a hook to the hole at the prow of each ship, I tied all the cords together at the end.

Meanwhile the enemy discharged several thousand arrows, many of which stuck in my hands and face. My greatest fear was for my eyes, which I should have lost if I had not suddenly thought of the pair of spectacles which had escaped the emperor's searchers. These I took out and fastened upon my nose, and thus armed went on with my work in spite of the arrows, many of which struck against the glasses of my spectacles, but without any other effect than slightly disturbing them. Then, taking the knot in my hand, I began to pull; but not a ship would stir, for they were too fast held by their anchors. Thus the boldest part of my enterprise remained. Letting go the cord, I resolutely cut with my knife the cables that fastened the anchors, receiving more than two hundred shots in my face and hands. Then I took up again the knotted end of the cables to which my hooks were tied, and with great ease drew fifty of the enemy's largest men-of-war after me.

When the Blefuscudians saw the fleet moving in order

and me pulling at the end, they set up a scream of grief and despair that it is impossible to describe. When I had got out of danger, I stopped awhile to pick out the arrows that stuck in my hands and face, and rubbed on some of the same ointment that was given me at my arrival. I then took off my spectacles, and after waiting an hour, till the tide was a little fallen, I waded on to the royal port of Lilliput.

The emperor and his whole court stood on the shore awaiting me. They saw the ships move forward in a large half-moon, but could not discern me, who, in the middle of the channel, was under water up to my neck. The emperor concluded that I was drowned and that the enemy's fleet was approaching in a hostile manner. But he was soon set at ease, for, the channel growing shallower every step I made, I came in a short time within hearing, and holding up the end of the cable by which the fleet was fastened, I cried in a loud voice: "Long live the most puissant Emperor of Lilliput!" The prince received me at my landing with all possible joy and made me a nardal on the spot, which is the highest title of honor among them. His majesty desired that I would take some opportunity to bring all the rest of his enemy's ships into his ports, and seemed to think of nothing less than conquering the whole empire of Blefuscu and becoming the sole monarch of the world. But I plainly protested that I would never be the means of bringing a free and brave people into slavery; and though the wisest of the ministers were of my opinion, my open refusal was so opposed to his majesty's ambition that he could never forgive me. And from this time a plot began, between himself and those of his ministers who were my enemies, that nearly ended in my utter destruction.

About three weeks after this exploit there arrived an embassy from Blefuscu, with humble offers of peace, which was soon concluded, on terms very advantageous to our emperor. There were six ambassadors, with a train of about five hundred persons, all very magnificent. Having been privately told that I had befriended them, they made me a visit, and paying me many compliments on my valor and generosity, invited me to their kingdom in the name of their master, the emperor. I asked them to present my most humble respects to the emperor, their master, whose royal person I resolved to attend before I returned to my own country. Accordingly, the next time I had the honor to see our emperor, I desired his general permission to visit the Blefuscudian monarch. This he granted me, but in a very cold manner, of which I afterward learned the reason.

When I was just preparing to pay my respects to the Emperor of Blefuscu, a distinguished person at court, to whom I had once done a great service, came to my house very privately at night, and without sending his name desired admission. I put his lordship into my coat pocket, and giving orders to a trusty servant to admit no one, I fastened the door, placed my visitor on the table, and sat down by it. His lordship's face was full of trouble, and he asked me to hear him with patience in a matter that highly concerned my honor and my life. "You are aware," he said, "that Skyresh Bolgolam has been your mortal enemy ever since your arrival, and his hatred is increased since your great success against Blefuscu, by which his glory

as admiral is obscured. This lord and others have accused you of treason, and several councils have been called in the most private manner on your account. Out of gratitude for your favors, I procured information of the whole proceedings, venturing my head for your service, and this was the charge against you:

"First, that you, having brought the imperial fleet of Blefuscu into the royal port, were commanded by his majesty to seize all the other ships and to put to death all the Bigendian exiles, and also all the people of the empire who would not immediately consent to break their eggs at the smaller end. And that, like a false traitor to his most serene majesty, you excused yourself from the service on pretense of unwillingness to force the consciences and destroy the liberties and lives of an innocent people.

"Again, when ambassadors arrived from the court of Blefuscu, like a false traitor you aided and entertained them, though you knew them to be servants of a prince lately in open war against his imperial majesty.

"Moreover, you are now preparing, contrary to the duty of a faithful subject, to voyage to the court of Blefuscu.

"In the debate on this charge," my friend continued, "his majesty often emphasized the services you had done him, while the admiral and treasurer insisted that you should be put to a shameful death. But Reldresal, secretary for private affairs, who has always proved himself your friend, suggested that if his majesty would please to spare your life and only give orders to put out both your eyes, justice might in some measure be satisfied. At this Bolgolam rose up in a fury, wondering how the secretary dared desire to preserve the life of a traitor; and the treasurer, pointing out the expense of keeping you, also urged your death. But his majesty was graciously pleased to say that since the council thought the loss of your eyes too easy a punishment, some other might afterward be inflicted. And the secretary, humbly desiring to be heard again, said that as to expense, your allowance might be gradually lessened, so that for want of sufficient food you should grow weak and faint and die in a few months, when his majesty's subjects might cut your flesh from your bones and bury it, leaving the skeleton for the admiration of posterity.

"Thus, through the great friendship of the secretary, the affair was arranged. It was commanded that the plan of starving you by degrees should be kept a secret, but the sentence of putting out your eyes was entered on the books. In three days your friend the secretary will come to your house and read the accusation before you and point out the great mercy of his majesty, that only condemns you to the loss of your eyes—which, he does not doubt, you will submit to humbly and gratefully. Twenty of his majesty's surgeons will attend, to see the operation well performed, by discharging very sharp-pointed arrows into the balls of your eyes as you lie on the ground.

"I leave you," said my friend, "to consider what measures you will take; and, to escape suspicion, I must immediately return as secretly as I came."

His lordship did so, and I remained alone in great perplexity. At first I was bent on resistance, for while I had liberty I could easily with stones pelt the metropolis to pieces; but I soon rejected that idea with horror, remembering the oath I had made to the emperor and the favors I had received from him. At last, having his majesty's leave to pay my respects to the Emperor of Blefuscu, I resolved to take this opportunity. Before the three days had passed, I wrote a letter to my friend the secretary telling him of my resolution, and without waiting for an answer went to the coast, and entering the channel, between wading and swimming reached the port of Blefuscu, where the people, who had long expected me, led me to the capital.

His majesty, with the royal family and great officers of the court, came out to receive me, and they entertained me in a manner suited to the generosity of so great a prince. I did not, however, mention my disgrace with the Emperor of Lilliput, since I did not suppose that prince would disclose the secret while I was out of his power. But in this, it soon appeared, I was deceived.

5

Three days after my arrival, walking out of curiosity to the northeast coast of the island, I observed at some distance in the sea something that looked like a boat overturned. I pulled off my shoes and stockings, and wading two or three hundred yards, I plainly saw it to be a real boat, which I supposed might by some tempest have been driven from a ship. I returned immediately to the city for help, and after a huge amount of labor I managed to get my boat to the royal port of Blefuscu, where a great crowd of people appeared full of wonder at the sight of so prodigious a vessel. I told the emperor that my good fortune had thrown this boat in my way to carry me to some place where I might return to my native country, and begged his orders for materials to fit it up and leave to depart—which, after many kindly speeches, he was pleased to grant.

Meanwhile the Emperor of Lilliput, uneasy at my long absence (but never imagining that I had the least notice of his designs), sent a person of rank to inform the Emperor of Blefuscu of my disgrace. This messenger had orders to represent the great mercy of his master, who was content to punish me with the loss of my eyes, and who expected that his brother of Blefuscu would have me sent back to Lilliput, bound hand and foot, to be punished as a traitor. The Emperor of Blefuscu answered with many civil excuses. He said that, as for sending me bound, his brother knew it was impossible. Moreover, though I had taken away his fleet, he was grateful to me for many good offices I had done him in making the peace. But that both their majesties would soon be made easy, for I had found a prodigious vessel on the shore, able to carry me on the sea, which he had given orders to fit up, and he hoped in a few weeks both empires would be free from me.

With this answer the messenger returned to Lilliput, and I (though the monarch of Blefuscu secretly offered me his gracious protection if I would continue in his service) hastened my departure, resolving never more to put confidence in princes.

In about a month I was ready to take leave. The Emperor of Blefuscu, with the empress and the royal family, came out of the palace, and I lay down on my face to kiss their hands, which they graciously gave me. His majesty presented me with fifty purses of sprugs (their greatest gold coin) and his picture at full length, which I put immediately into one of my gloves, to keep it from being hurt. Many other ceremonies took place at my departure.

I stored the boat with meat and drink and took six cows and two bulls alive, with as many ewes and rams, intending to carry them into my own country; and to feed them on board I had a good bundle of hay and a bag of corn. I

would gladly have taken a dozen of the natives, but this was a thing the emperor would by no means permit, and besides a diligent search into my pockets, his majesty pledged my honor not to carry away any of his subjects, though with their own consent and desire.

Having thus prepared all things as well as I was able, I set sail. When I had made twenty-four leagues, by my reckoning, from the island of Blefuscu, I saw a sail steering to the northeast. I hailed her, but could get no answer; yet I found I gained upon her, for the wind slackened, and in half an hour she spied me and discharged a gun. I came up with her between five and six in the evening on the 26th of September, 1701, and my heart leaped within me to see her English colors. I put my cows and sheep into my pockets and got on board with all my little cargo. The captain received me with kindness and asked me to tell him what place I came from last, but at my answer he thought I was raving. However, I took my black cattle and sheep out of my pocket, which, after great astonishment, clearly convinced him.

We arrived in England on the 13th of April, 1702. I stayed two months with my wife and family, but my eager desire to see foreign countries would suffer me to remain no longer. While in England I made great profit by showing my cattle to persons of quality and others, and before I began my second voyage I sold them for six hundred pounds. I left one thousand five hundred pounds with my wife and fixed her in a good house; then, taking leave of her and my boy and girl, with tears on both sides, I sailed again in search of further adventure.

The House
That
Jack Built

A MOTHER GOOSE RHYME

illustrated by
LEONARD WEISGARD

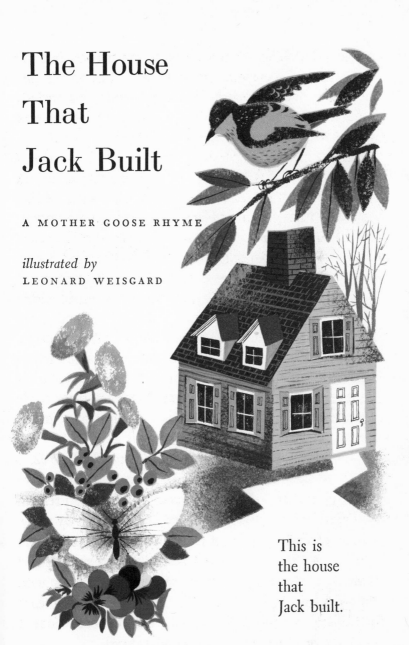

This is
the house
that
Jack built.

This is the malt
That lay in the house that Jack built.

This is the rat,
That ate the malt
That lay in the house that Jack built.

This is the cat,
That killed the rat,
That ate the malt
That lay in the house
that Jack built.

This is the dog,
That worried the cat,
That killed the rat,
That ate the malt
That lay in the house that Jack built.

This is the cow with the crumpled horn,
That tossed the dog,
That worried the cat,
That killed the rat,
That ate the malt
That lay in the house that Jack built.

This is the maiden all forlorn,
That milked the cow with the crumpled horn,
That tossed the dog,
That worried the cat,
That killed the rat,
That ate the malt
That lay in the house that Jack built.

This is the man all tattered and torn,
That kissed the maiden all forlorn,
That milked the cow with the crumpled horn,
That tossed the dog,
That worried the cat,
That killed the rat,
That ate the malt
That lay in the house that Jack built.

41

This is the priest all shaven and shorn,
That married the man all tattered and torn,
That kissed the maiden all forlorn,
That milked the cow with the crumpled horn,
That tossed the dog,
That worried the cat,
That killed the rat,
That ate the malt
That lay in the house that Jack built.

This is the cock that crowed in the morn,
That waked the priest all shaven and shorn,
That married the man all tattered and torn,
That kissed the maiden all forlorn,
That milked the cow with the crumpled horn,
That tossed the dog,
That worried the cat,
That killed the rat,
That ate the malt
That lay in the house that Jack built.

43

This is the farmer sowing his corn,
That kept the cock that crowed in the morn,
That waked the priest all shaven and shorn,
That married the man all tattered and torn,
That kissed the maiden all forlorn,
That milked the cow with the crumpled horn,
That tossed the dog,
That worried the cat,
That killed the rat,
That ate the malt
That lay in the house that Jack built.

Giddy-ap, Giddy-ap!

by CHARLOTTE STEINER

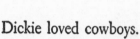

Dickie loved cowboys.
He loved to watch the brave cowboys on television.
He loved to see them save people.

When he wasn't watching cowboys Dickie pretended
he was a cowboy. That is why everybody called him
"Giddy-ap, Giddy-ap."

Dickie had a hobbyhorse to ride.
He had a popgun.
But he didn't have a cowboy suit.
So one day his grandma bought one.
Alas! It didn't fit at all.
It was so big,
and Dickie was so small.

Then Giddy-ap Dickie had an idea. He looked in the closet.
He found a big hat. He put it on.

Dickie looked a little bit like a
cowboy.
He found a leather belt.
He put it on.
Dickie looked even more like a
cowboy.
Then he found some fringe
from an old curtain.
His mother sewed it on his
pants.
Then Dickie *really* looked like
a cowboy.

46

And he felt like a brave cowboy. So Giddy-ap, Giddy-ap
galloped away to save someone.

Suddenly he saw a frog all wet in a puddle.
"I will save you, Mr. Froggy," Giddy-ap Dickie said.
And he carried the froggy into the house to dry

Slippety-slish! Froggy jumped out of Dickie's hands and hopped around the room. Dickie couldn't catch him.

Up! Froggy jumped on a chair and sat like company.

48

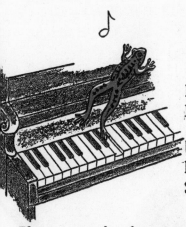

Hop! he jumped on the piano.
Ping! said the piano.

Down! he jumped on the table.
Plop! he went into a teacup.
Splash! went the tea.

Plop! went the frog into the cream pitcher. And all drippety-drip from the cream—he gave a great big jump onto the ironing board—and onto the clean shirt. Then away Froggy jumped out the window and back to his puddle. Froggy didn't need to be saved. So Giddy-ap, Giddy-ap galloped off to save someone else.

Suddenly he heard barking.
A big dog was chasing three little puppies.

"Oh, puppies, I will save you," cried Dickie,
and he opened the garden gate.
Into the yard they tumbled, and
Dickie slammed the gate.

The puppies were very lively.
They raced about.
They pulled Dickie's
cowboy pants.

52

They pulled and tugged and down went Dickie.
Away went the puppies, over Dickie,
over Dickie's cowboy hat
and into the kitchen.

They smelled Dickie's lunch.
One puppy lapped Dickie's milk.
One puppy gobbled Dickie's meat.
One puppy finished Dickie's carrots
and potatoes.

Then off they raced.
One puppy chased the cat.
One puppy pulled the curtain.
One puppy tipped over the lamp.

And out of the house scampered
the three little puppies.

There was the big dog waiting for them. She was very
glad to see them because she was their mother.

The three little puppies
didn't need
to be saved.
So Giddy-ap,
Giddy-ap
galloped off
to save someone else.

When he came to the pond he saw a baby duck waddling
toward the water.

"I won't let the baby duck drown," said Giddy-ap Dickie.
"I will save her with my lasso."

He threw his lasso.
He heard a fierce hiss.

It was the mother duck.
She flapped her wings and chased Dickie away.
And away swam the little duck with her mother. The little
duck didn't need to be saved. So Giddy-ap, Giddy-ap
galloped off to save someone else.

Dickie's canary bird was sitting in
its cage.
"You don't wan't to be locked up
all the time, do you?" said Dickie.
"I will save you."
So Giddy-ap, Giddy-ap opened the
cage door and the canary flew out
the window.

Dickie ran after her to see
where she was going.

The canary flew right in a
neighbor's window. Dickie's
little friend Doris said, "Here
is your bird. She is safe in my
cage."
The canary bird didn't need
to be saved.
And Giddy-ap, Giddy-ap was
tired of saving.
"Let's play hide-and-seek,"
he said to Doris.

Doris was "It." Dickie hid high up in a tree. Then Doris started looking for Dickie. She looked behind the fence. She looked under a barrel. Finally she opened the door of the shed.

Out came a big nannygoat chasing Doris. Dickie leaned out of the tree to see what was happening. Just then Doris and the nannygoat ran past the tree.

Dickie leaned so far that PLOP! down he fell onto the goat's back. Dickie was so surprised he hung on. The goat was so surprised that he stopped running. Doris stopped running, too.

"Oh, Giddy-ap, Giddy-ap,
you have saved me.
You are a *brave*
cowboy!"
said Doris.

Cinderella

by CHARLES PERRAULT

illustrated by SUSANNE SUBA

A very long time ago there lived a fair young girl with her father and mother in a beautiful home in the city. She was as happy as she was good, and she had all that heart could wish. But, by and by, a sad day came, and then many sad days. Her mother fell sick and died; and then, some time after, her father married again, for he said that his daughter must have someone to take care of her.

After that everything went wrong. The new mother was very cross and unkind; and she had two daughters of her own who were as cross and unkind as she was. They were harsh and cruel to the fair young girl and made her do all the hard work about the house.

She swept the floors and scrubbed the stairs and washed the dishes and cleaned the grates, while her two sisters sat in the parlor or lay asleep on their soft beds. They slept in

Adapted from James Baldwin's *Fairy Stories and Fables.*

fine rooms where there were long looking-glasses in which they could see themselves from head to foot; but she was sent to lie on an old pile of straw in the attic where there was only one chair, and no looking-glass at all.

When her day's work was done, they did not allow her to come into the parlor, but made her sit in the chimney corner in the kitchen among the ashes and cinders. This is why they nicknamed her Cinderella, or the cinder maid. But, for all her shabby clothes, she was handsomer by half than they could ever be.

Now it happened that the King's son gave a ball, and he invited all the fine rich people in the city to come to it. Of course, Cinderella's sisters were to go; and they were very proud and happy, for they thought that perhaps the Prince would dance with them. As for Cinderella, it only meant more work for her; she must help her sisters get their fine dresses ready, and she must iron their laces and ribbons, and starch their linen, and put their ruffles in order. For days and days they talked of nothing but clothes.

"I am going to wear my blue velvet dress, and trim it with point lace," said the elder.

"And I am going to wear my pink satin, with diamonds and pearls," said the younger.

And then they began to quarrel; and they would have fought, if Cinderella had not tried to make peace between them.

In the evening, while she was helping them with their hair, the elder said, "Cinderella, don't you wish you were going to the ball tonight?"

"Ah, you are only laughing at me," she said. "It is not

for me to go to as fine a place as that."

"You are right," said her sister. "Folks would think it very funny to see such a creature as you at a ball. The best place for you is among the ashes."

The sisters had laced themselves very tightly, for they wanted to look slender; and they had eaten scarcely anything for two days. It is no wonder, then, that they were more ill-tempered that night than they had been before; and they scolded and fretted and frowned until there was no getting along with them at all. But Cinderella was as sweet and kind as ever, and seemed to take all the more pains to make them look handsome.

At last the coach stopped at the door; they hurried out, and climbed into it; and away they went to the ball.

As for Cinderella, she sat down by the kitchen fire and cried.

All at once her Fairy Godmother stood before Cinderella and asked her what was the matter.

"I wish I could—I wish I could——" and that was all that Cinderella could say for weeping and sobbing.

"I know," said the Fairy Godmother. "You want to go to the ball, don't you?"

"Y-yes," cried Cinderella; and then she sobbed harder than ever.

"Well," said the Fairy, "I know you are a good girl, and I think we can manage it." Then she said, "Run into the garden and fetch me a pumpkin."

Cinderella did not stop to ask why, but ran out and soon brought in the finest pumpkin that she could find. Her Fairy Godmother quickly scooped out the inside of it, and struck it with her wand.

What a strange thing happened then! Before you could snap your fingers, the pumpkin was changed into a fine coach gilded all over and lined with red satin.

"Now fetch me the mouse trap from the pantry," said the Fairy Godmother.

Cinderella did so; there were six fat mice in it. The Fairy lifted the trap door and, as the mice came out one by one, she touched them with her wand. You would have laughed to see how quickly they were changed into fine black horses.

"But what shall we do for a coachman, my Cinderella?" said the Fairy Godmother.

"Maybe there is a rat in the rat trap," said Cinderella. "We might make a coachman of him."

"You are right," said the Fairy. "Go and see!"

Cinderella soon brought the rat trap, and in it were three big rats. The Fairy Godmother chose the finest one among them and touched him with her wand; and, quick as a flash, he became the fattest, jolliest coachman that you ever saw.

"Now, go into the garden," said the Fairy, "and you will find six gray lizards behind the watering pot. Bring them to me."

She had no sooner done so than the Fairy touched them with her wand and turned them into six footmen, who stood in waiting behind the coach as if they had been footmen all their lives.

"Now then, my Cinderella," said the Fairy Godmother, "now you can go to the ball."

"What! In these clothes?" said Cinderella; and she looked down at her ragged frock and began to sob again.

The Fairy Godmother laughed, and touched her with
her wand. You should have seen what happened then.
Her clothes were turned into the finest cloth of gold and
silver, all beset with rich jewels; and on her feet were glass
slippers, the prettiest that ever were seen.

"Now, my Cinderella," said the Fairy, "you must be
off at once. But remember that if you stay a moment after

midnight, your carriage will be a pumpkin again, your coachman a rat, your horses mice, and footmen lizards, and you will be a ragged little cinder maid."

Then Cinderella stepped into her coach; the coachman cracked his whip; and away she was whirled to the ball.

Somebody had told the King's son that a beautiful Princess, whom nobody knew, was coming; so, when the coach stopped at the palace door, there he was, ready to help her out. He led her into the hall, where all the fine people stood aside to let her pass. "Ah! How beautiful she is! Ah! How lovely she is!" said one to another.

The King himself, old as he was, whispered to the Queen that he had never seen so fair a maiden; and all the ladies stared at her clothes, planning how they would make theirs after the same pattern. Then the music struck up, and the Prince led her out to dance with him; and she danced with so much modesty and grace that everyone thought her more lovely than before.

By and by a fine supper was served, but the young Prince could not eat a mouthful, for thinking of the beautiful Princess. Cinderella went and sat down by her sisters, and was very civil and kind to them. This made them proud and glad, for they did not know her, and they thought it wonderful to be noticed by so grand a lady.

While she was talking to them, Cinderella heard the clock strike a quarter to twelve, and she remembered what her Fairy Godmother had told her about staying till midnight. So she made haste to bid the King and Queen good night. Then she climbed into her coach, and was driven home.

68

She met the Fairy at the door and thanked her for her kindness; and the good Fairy Godmother told her that she might go the next night to the Queen's ball, to which the Prince had invited her.

A few minutes later, the two sisters came home and found Cinderella sitting in the chimney corner, rubbing her eyes as though she were very sleepy.

"Ah, how long you have stayed!" she said.

"Well, if you had been there you would have stayed as long," said one of the sisters. "The prettiest Princess that you ever saw was at the ball; and she talked with us and gave us bonbons."

"Who was she?" asked Cinderella.

"That's just what everybody would like to know," said the elder, whose name was Charlotte.

"Yes, the King's son would give the world to know who she is," said the younger, whose name was Caroline.

"I wish I could see her," said Cinderella. "Oh, dear Miss Charlotte, won't you let me go tomorrow? And, Miss Caroline, won't you lend me your yellow dress to wear?"

"What, lend my yellow dress to a cinder maid!" cried Caroline. "I'm not as foolish as that!" And the two sisters went proudly to their rooms.

When the next night came, and the two sisters went to the ball, so did Cinderella. Everybody thought her more beautiful than before. "Now remember twelve o'clock," were the Fairy Godmother's last words when she started.

The young Prince never left her side. The dancing was delightful, and the supper was delicious, and time flew fast. Before she had stayed half as long as she wished, Cinderella

heard the clock begin to strike twelve. She rose up and ran from the room like a wild deer. The Prince followed her; but when he reached the street he saw nobody there except a ragged little cinder girl whom he would not have touched for the world.

Cinderella reached home, tired, frightened, and cold, without carriage, coachman, or footman. Nothing was left of all her finery but one of her little glass slippers; the other had dropped in the King's hall as she was running away.

When the two sisters came home, Cinderella asked them if they had had a good time at the ball, and if the pretty Princess had been there.

"Yes," they told her; "but when the clock struck twelve, she ran away without bidding anybody good night; and she dropped one of her little glass slippers in the hall— the prettiest slipper that anybody ever saw. The King's son picked it up and put it into his pocket, as though it were the rarest treasure in the world. But nobody could find out which way the Princess went."

Cinderella climbed up the stairs to her wretched bed in the attic; and the next day she was at work, sweeping and scrubbing as hard as ever.

And now, what do you think happened next? The Prince sent men with trumpets all through the land to invite every young lady to try the little glass slipper; and he declared that he would marry the one whose foot the slipper would just fit.

Of course, hundreds and hundreds of young ladies tried it; but their feet were ever and ever so much too big. You

would have laughed to see the two sisters try the slipper, and to hear their sighs when they had to give up. Cinderella was very much amused, for she knew all the time that it was her slipper.

"Let me see if it will fit me," she said at last.

"What, you? Bah!" cried Charlotte, laughing.

"Go into the kitchen and clean the grates," said Caroline; and both of them tried to keep her from touching the slipper.

But the man who had been sent with the slipper said that he had orders to let every maiden in the land make the trial. So Cinderella sat down on a three-legged stool, and when he put the slipper on her foot, it fitted her as if it had been made of wax! Then she drew from her pocket the other slipper, and put it on her other foot.

At the same moment, in came the Fairy Godmother. She touched Cinderella with her wand, and she was no longer a cinder maid but a beautiful young lady, clad in silk and jewels.

When the two sisters found that Cinderella was the pretty Princess whom they had seen at the ball, they threw themselves at her feet to ask pardon for the unkind way in which they had treated her. She lifted them up kindly, and said that she forgave them, and wished them always to love her.

Some time afterwards, the young Prince and Cinderella were married; and they lived together happily for many, many years. As for the two sisters, Cinderella gave them rooms in the palace; and they left off their cross, ugly ways, and by and by became the wives of two rich dukes who were friends of the Prince.

Everybody Lends
Jerry Muskrat a Hand

by THORNTON BURGESS
illustrated by HERMAN B. VESTAL

Just who started it nobody seems to know; possibly
it was the Merry Little Breezes, who are forever trying
to do something for somebody else. Anyway, they
did a lot of whispering and giggling as they watched
Jerry Muskrat making ready to build his new house.

77

Afterward they danced away across the Green
Meadows. In a surprisingly short time all the little
people who live in the Green Meadows and in the
Green Forest seemed to know all about what was
going on at the Smiling Pool. And they all seemed
to have the same idea, which was, what do you think?
Why, to help Jerry Muskrat to build his new house.
That's what it was!

Jerry didn't ask for any help. Oh, my no! Such a
thought never entered the head of Jerry Muskrat.
You see, there isn't a lazy bone in Jerry's plump little
body.

78

Jerry Muskrat likes to work
  And though he likes to play,
He'll never, never, never shirk
  The duties of each day.

So, when old Mother Nature whispered in his ear
that he ought to build a new house and make ready
for a long, cold winter, Jerry started in to work right
away. He didn't even mind when Billy Mink and
Little Joe Otter made fun of him, but dug away
down in the mud at the place where his new house
was to be. Yes, he was a hard worker.

"What are you going to make it of?" asked Billy Mink, as he sat kicking his heels on the Big Rock.

"Mud and sticks and bulrushes and grass," replied Jerry Muskrat, as he started to swim to where the alders grow beside the Laughing Brook. There he found Peter Rabbit sitting on the bank.

"Hello, Peter Rabbit!" said Jerry Muskrat, as he began cutting young alder shoots. When he had all he could carry, he started to carry them over to where he was building his new house.

Pretty soon Jerry was back in the alder thicket

for another load, and there he found the very nicest, the very best kind of a surprise. Can you guess what it was? It was a great bundle of alder shoots all ready for him to push across the Smiling Pool. Yes, sir, there they were, and there was Peter Rabbit cutting more.

81

Jerry Muskrat was so surprised he could hardly believe his own eyes, and he actually stuttered as he asked: "Wha-wha-what does this mean, Peter Rabbit?"

Peter grinned more broadly than ever as he replied: "It means that I want to help you build that new house, Jerry Muskrat, and I am going to cut all the alder shoots you need." Peter kept on working.

Jerry Muskrat thanked Peter Rabbit and swam away with the alder shoots.

Pretty soon he needed some willow shoots. When he reached the place where the willows grew, he found another surprise—the nicest bundle of willow

shoots, all cut, and Johnny Chuck cutting more.

"You can't have all the fun to yourself, building your own house!" cried Johnny Chuck, his eyes sparkling.

And so it was that everybody tried to lend a hand. Even Danny Meadow Mouse cut bulrushes, and Billy Mink and Little Joe Otter pushed them over to the new house.

My! My! My! Such a busy time in the Smiling
Pool. And it was hard to tell who was happiest, Jerry
Muskrat or those who were helping him.

What do you think?

The Story Book of Wheels

by MAUD *and* MISKA PETERSHAM

ROLLERS

There was a time long, long ago when the early people of the world had no wheels of any kind. They had learned that it was easier to drag a load than to carry it, and they used sledges to do this. There is no picture or story of anything like a wheel until ancient people began building palaces and monuments of heavy stone. They made pictures on these old monuments, and from these pictures we know that slaves, working under a blazing hot sun, pulled the heavy stones on sledges. Then someone found that the load could be moved more easily if logs were put under the sledge. As it was pulled along with slaves straining at the ropes, other slaves would put wooden rollers, or logs, in

85

front, and then, when the sledge passed over these logs, the slaves would pick them up and put them in front of the load again. Still other slaves worked on a lever to help the sledge forward. One man standing on the great stone clapped his hands to give the signal for all to pull together.

From the logs rolling under the heavy sledges like this, so long ago, came one of the most important things in all the history of the world. This is the wheel. The wheel took the place of the rollers about six thousand years ago, and now it has a part in almost everything we do.

ROLLERS TURN INTO WHEELS

Probably the first wheels were just two slices cut from the roller or log and fastened to the two ends of a long piece of wood called an *axle*. The wheel and the axle both turned together but were held in place so that they could not roll out from under the sledge. This made a kind of cart. Later the axle was fastened to the bottom of the cart, and

only the wheels turned. Sometimes, too, a wheel was made of planks of wood fastened together and then roughly cut into a circle.

From the solid wheel came the wheel with spokes. By leaving holes in the wheel, the clumsy wheel was made lighter, and it was found that a stick could be stuck in the hole to help the cart forward over rough places. So wheels gradually became lighter and lighter.

After this came the beautiful wheel of the chariot, with light spokes. These were made with the greatest skill. Old Egyptian wall paintings show the making of chariot wheels.

Some of the wheels of long ago even had tires. Buried in the earth in Britain, tires of iron from ancient chariots have been dug up, and old chariot wheels have been found in Egypt with thick tires of twisted leather.

Thousands of years later came the wheels we know— the bicycle wheel with wire spokes and rubber tires, and the automobile and airplane wheels with great balloon tires of rubber.

CHARIOTS

The rollers fastened under the sledge made a cart. After those first crude carts came the chariot with its two wheels. We have many pictures of chariots from old stone carvings and pictures painted on walls by ancient people. In a different part of the world, other earlier people left strange carvings on rocks which show us that they also had horses and vehicles.

Many different countries had chariots, but they were all

very much alike. They were uncomfortable to ride in, but they could be driven at great speed. The sides were lower than the front; the floor was near the ground, and the back was open. Some chariots were very beautiful. They were inlaid with glittering gold and silver and were drawn by swift horses.

Many, many chariots were used in olden days. In the chariot in which only one man rode, the reins of his horse were tied about his waist so that his arms were free for throwing spears or shooting arrows. Chariots of some nations were large enough for a driver and a shield bearer.

An old carving shows us an Assyrian king hunting lions from his chariot.

The chariot spread from Egypt to other countries. Those of the Greeks were very light and beautiful. The chariots of the Romans were often made of bronze. Their racing chariots were pulled by four horses side by side. In the triumphal processions, the chariots of the Roman conquerors were drawn by lions or leopards or even bears or elephants.

The great Julius Caesar brought back to Rome, from conquered Britain, chariots which were larger and heavier than his own. Some of them, too, were built with cruel, sharp knives fastened to the wheels and body.

For thousands of years people rode in chariots. The oldest known vehicle in the world is a chariot found buried in the ruins of an ancient city. It is nearly six thousand years old. Its wheels are of wood held together with copper nails. On the front of this old chariot there is a beautiful copper ring for the reins.

EARLY WAGONS AND CARTS

The ancient people had different kinds of wagons and carts. There are wall pictures which show the Egyptians carrying off the carts and oxen of a conquered people.

The Romans had more kinds of carts and wagons than any nation of their time. They had farm carts and family wagons. And they built many roads so well that they lasted for hundreds of years.

There was one ancient wagon which was something like the covered wagon of our grandfathers. This was used by an ancient people called Scythians who had no towns or villages but who wandered about with their families and cattle. The heavy wagon had a top shaped like a beehive

and covered with the skins of beasts or with felt. The men rode on horseback, but the women and children rode in these wagons, which were drawn by many oxen. When a tribe settled in any place for a time, the tops were lifted off and used as tents.

An old Chinese picture shows a heavy cart pulled by men. From early days the Chinese have also used a one-wheeled vehicle somewhat like our wheelbarrow.

WOMEN AND CHILDREN RIDE

A long time passed and people no longer rode in the old two-wheeled chariots, but their wagons and carts were still very much the same. The creaking wagons were just boxes resting on the axles. Some were drawn by many horses but still they could go only as fast as the horses could pull them.

Long ago the French had a law forbidding men to ride in wagons. They were afraid that riding would make the men less fit and strong. So only the women and children rode in the wagons, and the men rode on horseback.

There is an old English picture which shows women riding in a very grand wagon drawn by many horses. It was uncomfortable to ride in, but it was painted and gilded and had carved wheels and beautiful tapestry and cushions.

KINGS AND QUEENS RIDE

The first coaches belonged only to kings and queens and the very rich. One of the first we read about was called a trembling coach. It was sent from the King of Hungary to the King of France. This coach probably was one of the first to be built with the body hung from posts or supports instead of resting right on the axles.

TRAVELERS RIDE

In the early days, very few people traveled except warriors. Later, nobles and important people made journeys in their own wagons, but the only conveyance for carrying travelers until the time of the stagecoach was the long wagon, a wagon with a cover but no springs. The passengers sat or lay on straw on the floor during the weary hours of the journey.

Later, stagecoaches were built to carry travelers on regular trips as do the buses and trains of today. In the beginning the roads were very bad, and the coach pitched over stones and into deep ruts and holes. In lonely places there was always the fear of robbers and highwaymen.

When springs were invented, there was much less jolting. The coaches of the rich and the stagecoaches for travelers became less clumsy and more comfortable.

Later Queen Elizabeth had a coach, and hers was one of the first in England. Her coach was gilded and carved, and she sat under a canopy of red velvet embroidered with pearls and gold. The sides were open so that her people could see her.

Queen Elizabeth was proud of her coach, but when she rode, she was jolted and jarred and knocked about. Later the royal coaches grew less clumsy but they were still just as magnificent. The nobles tried to outdo each other in the grandeur of their coaches.

WHEELS IN AMERICA

The Indians of North America never knew wheels. The earliest white settlers here traveled as the Indians did, on foot or by boat. The only roads were trails through the forest. But the English governors, who were sent from England to the colonies, brought their coaches with them. Roads were made between the larger towns. Later a few of the rich people of the colonies also had coaches, but most of the traveling was still done on horseback.

As the colonies grew and people wanted to go from place to place, stagecoaches like those in England began to be used. The first stagecoaches began to run between the larger cities about the time of George Washington. It took about a week to go from Boston to New York in a stagecoach at that time. The roads were rough and the coaches were uncomfortable. People rode inside and outside, and the baggage was piled on top. At first there was no glass in the windows; leather curtains kept out the storm and the cold. Often the passengers had to get out and walk or even push.

Another American vehicle was the covered wagon. This was first built by the Dutch farmers of Pennsylvania. It had a large, strongly-built body, high at both ends. The wheels were wide so that it would not sink easily into the mud. It had a great, rounded top made of canvas, which was tied down with ropes at the sides and ends. It was pulled by oxen or horses. Underneath the wagon hung the pails for watering the cattle and the bucket of tar which was used to grease the wheels.

When the settlers in the eastern part of this country started going westward into unknown country, they traveled in covered wagons. There were no roads and no bridges. Many wagons traveled together to protect the settlers from the Indians.

The few belongings that the settlers took with them for their new homes were piled in the wagon. The men rode on horseback beside the wagon, and the women and children rode inside. For months these wagons were their only homes.

Later, a light, two-wheeled vehicle called a *chaise* or *shay* was made in America. It had room for only one person. There is a story that it was first made for a selfish man who did not want to take anyone with him when he rode. Then came the four-wheeled, American-built buggy which was followed by the horseless carriage. This first horseless carriage was just a buggy with an engine.

BICYCLES

As more people rode, better roads were made, and a vehicle was built which the rider himself could make go. This was the bicycle, built with one wheel in front of the other. It was called a *hobby horse* or a *dandy horse*. It had no pedals and was so low that the rider made it go by striking his feet on the ground. People laughed at these dandy horses, and they soon went out of use.

After a while, pedals were added to bicycles. People then used the first popular bicycle, but it was so uncomfortable that it was called a *bone shaker*. It was made of solid iron with wooden wheels and iron tires.

Wire-spoked wheels with rubber tires came later. The early bicycles were built with a very large front wheel. But this bicycle upset so easily that it was dangerous to ride. Then came the safety bicycle that we know with its rubber tires. In some countries a great many people still ride bicycles.

MAKING THE WHEELS GO

In the very beginning men themselves dragged their sledges. Then for thousands of years horses and oxen and other animals furnished the power which made the wheels go. The power of the wind had been tried, and sails were put on a wagon. This, however, was never very successful on land. All these years, wheels turned at about the same speed. But as time became more and more important, people looked for ways to make wheels turn faster and faster. When new kinds of power were found to make the wheels go, the story of wheels changed to the story of speed.

FAST AND FASTER

This part of the story starts less than two hundred years ago. It was found that steam could be used to turn wheels. At first steam was used to turn the paddle wheels of boats. The first land vehicle which went with steam was a three-wheeled wagon built in France by a man named Cugnot. This was built to pull guns about. This three-wheeled wagon of Cugnot's was never used, but it did prove that steam could make vehicles go.

In different countries inventors made experiments, until at last in England a steam locomotive, or iron horse, was built which could pull coaches or wagons along tracks at the rate of fifteen miles an hour. Thus the story of speed started.

At the same time that England was experimenting with steam locomotives on tracks, she was building steam carriages which ran on the highways. The steam carriage looked like a coach but it had a boiler. People as well as horses were terror stricken at the sight of the strange, noisy vehicles dropping coals and driving horses and men off the roadways into the fields. There was great objection to them, and in England their use on the highways was forbidden. That stopped the development of horseless carriages for about one hundred years. The steam carriages disappeared, but railroads grew. The little, puffing locomotives with their strings of stagecoaches in time grew into fast, powerful trains.

HORSELESS CARRIAGES

But people wanted something which would run on roads as well as on a railroad track, and which would go faster than a horse. Steam carriages had been made in England. In 1861 a German, named Otto, had made an engine which burned gasoline. It was found that electricity also could be used to make vehicles go.

So inventors in different countries worked on with steam and gas and electricity. At last they built an engine small enough to be attached to a carriage or buggy. The result was the first horseless carriage.

Only fifty years ago the horseless carriage was a strange vehicle, frightening horses and laughed at by many. The

Barnum and Bailey Circus once had one as a curiosity to show the people.

Soon the horse was seen less and less often on the highway and the day of the horseless carriage had come.

At first the horseless carriage had large wheels, and the engine was under the body. It looked like a carriage or a buggy, and it is said that some of the first bodies still had the place for a horsewhip. The first American cars used steam or electricity, but soon gasoline came into use for power.

The horseless carriage became the automobile, and the design of the carriage changed. The engine was put in front, and the wheels were made smaller with great tires of rubber. Each year the cars changed in appearance until the low, streamlined cars came. Automobiles travel with great speed and comfort and cost so little that a great many people own them. Good roads now run to every part of the country. The automobile has entirely changed our way of living.

Now we live in a world on wheels. Speeding trains and ships bring faraway places close together. Motor buses that are comfortable and swift go from one end of the country to the other. Many, many people ride in automobiles of their own. There are also powerful tractors which pull and push loads and do all kinds of heavy work which men or animals used to do. Fast-turning propellers are wheels without rims. In the sky whirling propellers drive airplanes, and on the sea propellers push great ships.

More wheels turn in the United States than in any other country in the world.

WHEELS OF INDUSTRY

All the time that men were using wheels for their chariots, their carts, and their coaches, they were finding ways to make wheels help them with their work. The wheels of vehicles were turned by animal power, but wind and water as well as men and animals were used to turn working wheels.

An old picture shows a treadmill being turned by men who continually climbed steps placed on the inside of the wheel. Another picture of the same time shows how a

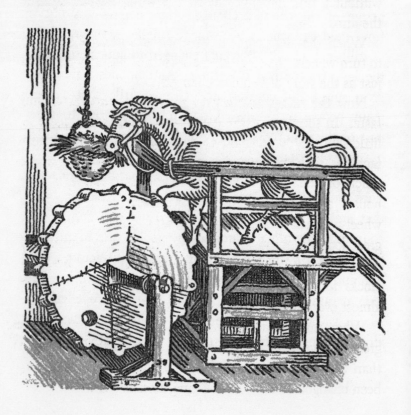

horse was used to turn a working wheel.

From early days until the time of our grandfathers, the spinning wheel was worked by hand or foot. The man who made dishes used his foot to turn the wheel on which he shaped them.

Long ago great wheels were built where streams ran swiftly, and the water turned the wheels. In this way water was pumped, or the grain was ground for the miller.

Grain was also ground into flour, or water was pumped by the windmill. The arms of the windmill make a wheel without a rim, and it turns by the wind pressing against the arms.

When the time came in which men used new powers to turn wheels, the story of the wheels of industry changed just as the story of vehicles changed.

Now the many, many working wheels turn faster and faster. In the days of the stagecoach, goods were made in little shops by hand. Now they are manufactured in great factories with millions of busy wheels of all sizes doing much of the work. The lumber of which some of our houses are built is cut with a circular saw. This is a wheel with sharp teeth along its edge. Cloth is woven on great looms worked with wheels. Our books are made on presses which use wheels and rollers. Our watches and clocks run with wheels. Wheels have a part in making almost everything about us.

When man made the first wheel, he made one of the greatest inventions of all time. Today wheels turn faster than they have ever turned before. The whole world has been changed and is still changing because of wheels.

Napoleon,
the Corsican Boy

by SMITH BURNHAM

illustrated by RICHARD MOSS

Text from *Hero Tales From History*, copyright, 1922, 1930, 1938, by The John C. Winston Company.

Though Napoleon Bonaparte was the greatest soldier of his time, he was small in body. His fullest height was a little above five feet. The story of his strange career shows how a poor, puny little lad made himself emperor of France and master of Europe, so that kings, generals, and prime ministers bowed, like so many servants, to his imperial will.

He began, while he wore petticoats, to wish to be a soldier. He threw away his baby rattle for a brass cannon, and his first playthings were little iron soldiers. When he was old enough to play with other boys, he always chose to be a soldier and, small as he was, he was the one who told the bigger boys just what to do. Even then, if his mother gave him a piece of cake, he would go out to the edge of the little town and trade it to an old soldier for some coarse, black army bread. As he grew older, this soldier-longing became his ambition. His health was never very good. He was often nervous, willful, and hard to manage. But he had a keen sense of honor, and always despised a coward.

Napoleon's home was the rugged island of Corsica. While he was still a little boy, he found, between some rocks near the shore, a cave which he claimed for his own. This is still pointed out, to thousands who come to visit the boy's birthplace, as "Napoleon's Grotto."

At that time there was a feud between the boys of the

town and the shepherd lads on the hills around. Little Napoleon told the other town boys that if they would do as he said, he would make those big country boys stop throwing stones at them whenever they met. The town lads agreed to this; so Napoleon told them to gather stones and pile them in a row a little distance below the fortress which the shepherds had chosen behind some rocks on top of their hill.

The pale Bonaparte boy led his young army up till the country youths fired a volley of stones at them. Then he turned and ran down the hill followed by his company. The enemy came out and gave chase, pell-mell. This was just what Napoleon expected. When the little leader got down to the piles of stones he shouted—*"Halt!"*

His soldiers obeyed.

"Stones!"

Each boy gathered up as many as he could carry.

"About face!—FIRE!"

Before the astonished shepherds could stop, they were met by a shower of rocks. The big fellows broke and scattered in all directions, and two of them were taken prisoner. Captain Bonaparte would not let them go till the other country boys pledged themselves not to touch his "men" again.

Thus eight-year-old Napoleon became the leader of the boys in his home town.

Before he was ten, he was sent to a military school in France, where sons of noblemen were educated. Some of those French boys were wayward, mean, and savagely cruel. They made fun of the shy country lad, for his rough Corsican ways and speech, and because he was small and sallow. Napoleon had entered the school on a scholarship,

so they sneered at him as "the charity boy." He could not speak French at first, and pronounced his own name so that it sounded like the French words for "nose of straw." As Napoleon's nose was long, straight, and thin, they laughed and shouted his nickname, "Mr. Straw Nose!"

All this made the proud, sensitive lad speechless with rage. He kept himself away from the rest. A garden plot was assigned for each cadet to tend. A few of the others were too idle to take care of theirs, so they gave them to Napoleon and he kept them in order as his own. In the center of his little kingdom he built an arbor where he could stay alone to study and plan as he had done in his little cave in Corsica, and woe to those who entered there without his permission. He had suffered this sort of life

nearly four years before his father and mother managed to visit their boy, who was almost a prisoner in military school. Napoleon wrote of the shock the visit gave his mother:

"When she came to see me at Brienne, she was frightened at my thinness. I was indeed much changed, because I employed the hours of recreation in working, and often passed the nights in thinking about the days' lessons. My nature could not bear the idea of not being first in my class."

After finishing at this academy, Napoleon went to the military college at Paris. Father Bonaparte's death, about this time, left the family poorer than ever. Sometimes Napoleon did not have enough to eat. But that did not prevent him from studying hard. His great ambition kept him from starving. Some time after his graduation, he was assigned to a small command in Paris. "Red" revolutionists were trying to destroy the city. Young Napoleon thought it high time to stop them. A mob gathered in a public square, threatening to kill people and burn their houses. He opened fire on the mob and cleared that square in short order. It was said afterward, "Bonaparte stopped the French Revolution with a whiff of grapeshot!"

From being "the Man of the Hour" Napoleon went on till he became "the Man of Destiny." He was raised to the highest rank, and as General Bonaparte became commander-in-chief of the French army in Italy, where he gained brilliant victories over the Austrians. But the Austrians would not stay beaten, and while Napoleon was away in Egypt, Austria started to win back its control of northern Italy.

When Napoleon returned to Paris he was the idol of the people. They elected him consul, a kind of president, of the French republic. The Austrians were pleased at this, as it would keep "the Little Corporal," as the soldiers called Napoleon, in Paris. He would have to send another commander to Italy, and the Austrians had gotten such a start that they could win the victory before the French forces could go around the Alps.

Austria was already crowing over its triumph and all Europe was laughing because General Bonaparte had been "caught napping," when one May morning Consul Napoleon and a great army came tobogganing down the mountain-sides into the plains of Italy, as if they had fallen from the sky.

In a letter to his older brother, Napoleon wrote of this: "We have dropped here like a thunderbolt; the enemy didn't expect it, and hardly believe it yet."

He had made his soldiers climb up the Alps Mountains in the highest, steepest place, dragging heavy cannon and army supplies after them. By his wonderful feat of crossing the Alps, Napoleon won by surprise the victory at Marengo, just as he had beaten the shepherd lads when he was a boy of eight.

The people now made their hero consul for life. After that it was easy for him to make himself Emperor of the French. At his coronation Napoleon snatched the crown out of the hands of the Pope and placed it on his own head, to show that he was Emperor by the right of his own might. Yet Emperor Napoleon kept on leading his armies in per-

son. He still had to fight with other nations to hold his place as master of Europe. He gained even more brilliant victories, as Emperor Napoleon, than he had won as General Bonaparte. Not content with his record as a great conqueror, he gave the French people the *Code Napoléon*; a set of laws which proved him to be also a wise statesman and lawgiver.

The kings and nobles of Europe always hated Napoleon. They said he was vulgar, and called him "the Corsican upstart." But the French people loved him as one of themselves. No general or emperor ever had more devoted followers than Napoleon Bonaparte. Millions of men gave their lives willingly to fight his battles. He waged war after war till there were but few fighting men left in France. Then the people began to think that Napoleon loved them because they could help him win victories to give him more power and fulfill his high ambition. They began to say among themselves, "He is sacrificing us for his own glory." While at the height of his power, Napoleon exclaimed, "What are a million lives to a man like me!"

When the people lost their faith in him, Napoleon began to lose instead of win his battles. Generals and nobles

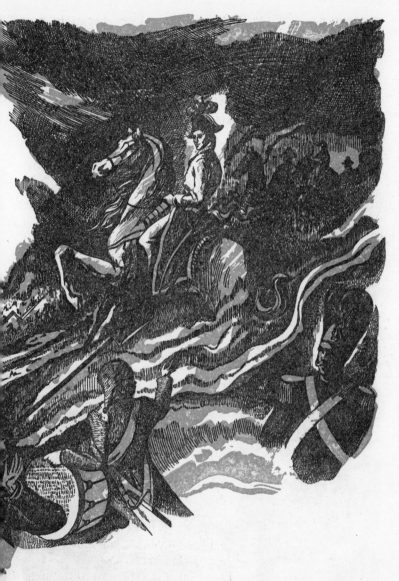

stopped flattering him and began to fight him. His own
brothers and sisters, whom he had made kings and queens,

deserted him. Even his wife forsook him, taking with her his only son, the idol of his heart.

Napoleon's last battle was at Waterloo, in Belgium. Because this loss brought ruin to him, the name of the place became a kind of proverb. When overwhelming defeat comes to a great man, people say, "He has met his Waterloo!"

The conquered conqueror was taken prisoner and sent thousands of miles away as a captive to the bleak island of St. Helena. He made the best of his hard lot as "the fortunes of war." But as a friendless conqueror, he had to endure long years of loneliness. All his life he had been selfish and merciless. His reward was banishment.

THE TRIGGERFISH DEFENDS HIMSELF WITH A SHARP BACK-FIN

Fishes of
the Shallow Sea

There are thousands of different kinds of fish in the world's oceans. Some of them are forty feet long. Others are hardly bigger than your fingernail. But there are more strangely colored and queerly shaped species in the waters of the shallow tropical seas than anywhere else.

Among the true beauties of these shallow seas are the Queen Triggerfish. Their mouths seem too small for their bodies, and their tails as well as their top and bottom fins have beautifully curved edges. Most of their lives are

A SKATE IS FLAT   THE QUEEN ANGELFISH

spent around the many-colored coral "forests" that rise from the sea's bottom. This is the reason for their numerous lovely colors, which serve as camouflage to hide them from their enemies. They can change these hues, too, to match those of the coral and the water wherever they are swimming. A most unusual three-piece "lock" keeps one sharp fin stiff and erect for protection.

Some Are Beautiful, Some Dangerous

Skates are entirely different from such gorgeous fishes. Skates spend most of their lives on the ocean floor and so, for protection, their backs are nearly the color of the sand. They have long, whip-like tails, and some of them carry a sharp spine. Their small mouths are underneath, and they swim by moving the outer ends of their very broad, pointed "wings" up and down as if they were flying. Actually, these "wings" are specially shaped fins. Another surprising thing about skates is that they are relatives of the sharks. Their family is one of the oldest in the whole fish kingdom.

The Queen Angelfish is as different from a skate as day is from night. From side to side he is almost as thin as a shingle, but from back to belly he may measure twice the size of your open palm. That thin, bluish line from front to back near the top of the body is caused by a hidden tube containing delicate nerves by means of which the fish can probably "hear" very low underwater sounds.

In these same waters lives another completely different fellow, the Green Moray. He is a huge, powerful eel with wicked jaws that can give his foe a terrific bite. He looks somewhat like a snake, but is actually a very ancient type of fish. Since Morays live mostly in dark openings among the coral, they have no need of bright colors to conceal them from any creatures foolish enough to attack them.

MORAYS ARE DANGEROUS EELS   THE ANCIENT COWFISH

If you compare the picture of this giant eel with the Cowfish beside it, you will get an even better idea of the great differences among the fishes of these tropical seas. The bump between the popeyes of a Cowfish gives him a sort of cow-like expression; his stomach is very broad and flat, while his back stands up in a sharp ridge. And, for hiding among white coral masses, the Cowfish changes his blues and yellows to match them. The Cowfish has ancestors who lived over fifty million years ago!

A healthy, well-fed Porkfish, like the one on this page, is almost unbelievably colorful. One of the oddest things about him is that wavy, reddish pattern where his tail begins. This, and the two dark brown bands in front, are part of his camouflage uniform. Fooling the enemy is also the purpose of the black streak in front and the black spot

GLISTENING COLORS GIVE PORKFISH AN AMAZING BEAUTY

THE BUTTERFLY FISH APPEARS TO SWIM BACKWARDS

near the tail of the Four-eyed Butterfly Fish. These give you the idea that this little three-incher is swimming tail-first, exactly opposite to the direction in which he is really going.

Water Pigs and Water Horses

Eating little snails and shellfish while standing on his head is a favorite habit of the very peculiar Hogfish. His meals live on the pale floor of the shallow sea, so the Hogfish is light-colored, too. This strange method of rooting for food explains the name which has been given to this fish.

Seahorses are perhaps the weirdest of all shallow-sea fishes. They really do not seem to be fishes at all, for their fins are extremely small and their necks and heads suggest

THE HOGFISH AT LUNCH   A TEAM OF SEAHORSES

those of horses. Also, they curl their tails around coral
branches and seaweed stems as if they were monkeys. When
they swim they float upright in the water and go very slowly,
because they have only one back fin to work with. But
few marine creatures can match their ability to change
colors according to the conditions around them.

Seahorses, like regular fishes, lay eggs. But their way of
hatching them is truly amazing. When the female lays the
eggs they are placed in a special sack inside the male's body,
where they stay until hatching time comes.

Various kinds of seahorses are found in all of the world's
tropical seas. They can travel long distances, too, by hiding
in masses of floating seaweed and just drifting along. One
of the strangest species comes from a region near the coast
of Africa. This kind has lived for so many thousands of

years among long, coarse seaweeds that he has developed ribbon-like streamers which closely resemble those of the plants which surround it. It takes very sharp eyes to tell which is seahorse and which is seaweed. This little pony-like fish is a master in the art of camouflage.

Where Do We Eat?

Every fish is built to succeed in the kind of place where he lives and to eat the sort of food that is found there. So there are good reasons for the peculiar shape of the Look-down Fish. This odd species reminds you of a piece of board floating on edge. A specimen eight inches long is about six inches high but only a half-inch thick. No wonder he can easily look down to see if there is any food below him.

Another thin, surprising bottom-feeder is the Peacock Flounder. When he is very young, he swims on edge like the Lookdown. But in a few days he begins to lean over on one side. At the same time the eye on the lower side of his head starts moving toward its companion on the top side.

LOOKDOWNS DO JUST THAT

FLOUNDERS ARE GOOD EATING

THE ROCK BEAUTY IS COLORFULLY DRESSED

Finally both eyes are on the same side where they can watch upward while their owner feeds flat on the bottom of the sea.

Some other kinds of flounders are found far north of the tropical shallow seas. These Northerners are great favorites with fisherman, who call the big ones Flatfish or sometimes Doormats. When properly cooked they taste delicious.

The Rock Beauty, on this page, is related to the Butterfly and Angelfish. He is very showy, too. But that big black blotch on his side makes him look less like a fish and more like a dark shadow in the coral reefs where he lives. This is another of Nature's ways to protect some living creatures from enemies which might otherwise capture and eat them.

124

Dick and the Canal Boat

by SANFORD TOUSEY

illustrated by EDWARD SHENTON

Dick Sefton was galloping a brown mule all over his father's north field. He had no saddle. Bareback was good enough for him. He had not bothered even to put a bridle with a bit on the mule. He just threw the loose end of the halter rope across its neck, tied that end to the halter ring, and he was ready to go.

Dick had been riding animals since he was big enough to be lifted onto one by his father, who traded in horses. The big pasture where Mr. Sefton kept his horses until he sold them had been Dick's playground. And the horses and mules, even occasional ponies his father pastured there, had been his only playmates, for the Sefton cottage was on the outskirts of Albany and there weren't many neighbors.

Dick had to learn when he was a little boy that he couldn't keep a pony, even though it was a pet. His father explained to him that the sale of the animals gave him a profit. This profit was what paid for Dick's food and clothing. So Dick said goodbye to his pet when he had to and welcomed the new ones when they came. And in between times he begged his father for stories about the places where the horses went.

More than anything else he liked to hear about the horses that were taken to the Canal Boat Basin in Albany. All canal boaters who tied up in the basin at Albany knew of Mr. Sefton and his good horses. He was an honest horse dealer in a day when honest horse dealers were rare. He sold many of his horses to canal-boat captains. The animals were driven along the canal's towpath to pull the boats. Good mules were often used too. Dick had never been to the Canal Boat Basin, but the canal boats sounded very exciting. Riding a canal-boat horse and living on a canal boat would be real adventure, he was certain.

Dick was thinking about the canal boat today as he rode Jinny. Jinny was one of a lively team—Jack and Jinny—both fine mules that had been well cared for, and he had heard his father say he planned to sell them to Captain Erwin of the *Ella E.*, who was in need of a team.

Dick patted Jinny's back.

"You'll be seeing the canal boats and the whole Erie Canal soon," he said wistfully. "Just imagine pulling a canal boat all the way to Buffalo."

Dick was up early the next morning to give Jack and Jinny a goodbye pat. His father noticed the wishful look in Dick's eyes. Dick could hardly believe his ears when his father said, "You may ride Jinny to Albany if you're willing to sit behind me on Ginger coming home. You're big enough now to see a bit of the world."

Dick jumped at the chance to see the canal basin and the boats, too! What a wonderful sight they must be. These boats traveled three hundred and sixty-three miles away by inland waterway.

Quickly Dick changed to his good clothes. After a parting hug from his mother he jumped onto Jinny's back and they were off up the dusty road to

Albany. Mr. Sefton led Jack by his halter rope. They rode past prosperous farms and over noisy wooden bridges. Farmers waved to them from the fields, for many of them knew Mr. Sefton.

It seemed no time at all to the happy Dick when they came in sight of Albany's church steeples and the state capital.

But most exciting to Dick was the view of the canal-boat basin. There many boats were tied up before starting their return trips. A captain from one boat visited another. On a few idle boats checkers and card games were going on. On other boats there were noise and bustle as trucks brought loads of freight. Wash lines were up and clothes of many colors dried in the breeze. Smoke came from the tin chimneys attached to cookstoves in the galleys below. Captains' wives were getting food ready for hearty eaters.

Dick was feeling hungry by the time Mr. Sefton found the *Ella E.* They tied their animals to stanchions along the wharf. Captain Erwin greeted them and looked the mules over; then he led Dick and his father down several steps into the cozy cabin. Gyp, the dog, sniffed at them. Near the stove was a mother cat with three kittens.

Mrs. Erwin, called Ma Erwin by the canalers, was just opening the oven door. She took out a hot apple pie. After placing it on the table she greeted Dick and Mr. Sefton.

"How good that pie smells," thought Dick.

Ma Erwin saw his longing look toward the pie.

"You must have a piece right now!" she exclaimed, cutting it generously.

Dick finished every crumb and sighed happily. A canal boat was just as much fun as he had expected.

The light in the comfortable cabin came from windows up above the men's heads. Captain Erwin and Mr. Sefton sat down at the table to agree on the price for the mules. When this was done Captain Erwin pushed open a small panel in the woodwork of the cabin. He took out a leather pouch and Dick heard the clink of gold pieces inside it.

"I got these from the bank this morning," explained the captain. "I don't usually leave so much lying around. But I knew you'd be here. I'll pay you half now and the other half after I've collected the money due me on this next trip. Money doesn't come in as plentiful as it did before they laid the Erie railroad tracks!"

Just as he finished speaking, they were all startled

by a noise at the window above.

They looked up in time to see an evil face with a red beard disappear.

"I don't like snoopers!" shouted the captain. He grabbed his shotgun from the pegs on the wall and rushed on deck. But the intruder was gone.

Dick was too busy to worry about intruders. He was interested in every detail of the *Ella E.*

"How I'd like to travel on this boat!" he remarked to his father.

"No reason why you shouldn't," replied Mrs. Erwin. "We need a boy on board. Maybe your pa will let you go?"

Mr. Sefton laughed. "Now I know why Dick has always begged to see the canalers. I guess he was hoping for a chance to travel. And I guess as long as it's vacation time he might as well go along. It'll do him good to get away from home for a spell."

They went out on the wharf and got Jack and Jinny. It took a little urging to persuade the mules to cross the plank and enter their new stalls. When they balked, Dick took Jinny's halter rope and talked to her. She and Dick finally crossed and Jack followed.

"That boy has a way with the critters," remarked Captain Erwin admiringly, as Dick led the mules

into their stalls in the fore part of the boat. There were two other stalls occupied by a sturdy team of horses.

"Come here, sonny," said the captain. "Here's your bunk, up top."

Dick looked into a snug little room next to the horse stalls. It contained two bunks, one above the other. On the wall opposite were pegs to hang clothes on.

Dick was delighted. He had always wanted to sleep in a real "upstairs" bunk. Now he had one.

"Ned, our deck hand, has the lower bunk. He'll be back soon. You'll like him," explained the captain.

Mr. Sefton told Dick to mind what the Erwins

told him. Then he shook hands, mounted Ginger, and was off for home.

He had scarcely gone when Ned, the deck hand, came aboard. Ned was young and had a happy smile. Dick felt that he was a friend from the start.

When dinnertime came at noon, Ma rang a big brass bell. They all sat down at the table covered with a red-and-white plaid tablecloth. And what a meal Ma brought from the little galley in the rear! Fried chicken and sweet potatoes, rolls hot from the oven, boiled onions, two kinds of pie, and all the milk Dick could drink, from a big glass pitcher.

Dick spent the afternoon going over the boat from bow to stern. It was a new world to him, and he didn't want to miss a thing.

"We'll turn in early tonight," ordered the captain soon after dark. "I want to be moving at daylight."

Dick felt very snug under the blanket in his cozy bunk. Ned woke him before dawn, but Ma Erwin already had breakfast ready. When the meal was over Dick went on deck with the captain. It would take skill to get the *Ella E.* past the other boats in the basin. Dick helped to harness the horses. Ned led them to the towpath. Captain Erwin tossed out the towline to which the team was then hitched tandem.

From long experience the horses bent to their task. Sparks flew from their shoes as the *Ella E.* slowly moved forward. The first few feet were the hardest. After that the boat pulled easier. As soon as she started to move, Captain Erwin took the tiller. When they had to pass another boat Dick was surprised to see Ma Erwin hurry forward and pull in the towline which Ned released from the team. As soon as they had floated past the other boat she tossed the rope back to Ned. He rehitched it to the horses, who began pulling again.

"Ma gives us a hand in a pinch," said Captain Erwin a bit proudly. He guided the *Ella E.* out of the basin and into the canal without bumping another boat. Dick stood beside him at the big tiller as he steered.

The captain saw Dick's interest. "Someday you can take the tiller," he said to Dick. "We'll give you your first lesson further up the canal. There's less traffic there."

They rode along in the early-morning light to the "clop, clop" of the horses' hoofs. Past the brick and frame buildings that lined the canal went the *Ella E.* Dick ran from the stern up to the bow. It was all so interesting he could not decide where to stay. As they

got out into the country he sat forward on the roof. He could listen to Ned now, for Ned had produced his harmonica and was riding comfortably on one of the horses as he played.

But suddenly Ned sprang to attention. Another team, pulling a boat, was coming right at them.

"Now they'll get tangled!" exclaimed Dick. But Ned slowed his team until his towline formed a great loop on the bottom of the canal. Over this the other boat passed. Ned kept his team on the outside. The other team stayed inside and stepped over Ned's line as they moved forward. It was done easily and neatly. Dick drew a breath of relief when he saw the lines all clear.

"I'll break your mules in after dinner," called Ned to Dick. "If they take kindly to the towpath maybe the captain will let you ride one after we have passed Schenectady."

Dick was pleased with that prospect. He would really be helping with the towing if the captain consented.

At noon they tied up to feed the horses and eat dinner. Then Ma brought out her workbasket. "Here, Dick," she said, "is a pair of Ned's old blue denim britches I've cut down for you. You shouldn't be around horses with those good britches on. Go change."

Dick thanked the kindly Ma Erwin. He was glad to have a pair of overalls. He felt much more like a real canaler in them.

As they passed beautiful, prosperous-looking New York farms, the farmers' wives came down to the canal to sell their chickens, eggs, preserves, butter, cheeses, or even a side of pork. Many trips over the Erie Canal had made Ma acquainted with the countrywomen and their ways. She had a long pole with an old parasol tied to it. The parasol was open and hung upside down at the end of the pole. Into this the housewives placed their produce, for Ma always looked at the goods before she paid. From it they took their money after the bartering was finished. Dick helped her swing the pole back to the boat when the parasol was heavily loaded. Ma never failed to ask about any ailing members of the farmer's family.

Later Ma gave the captain and Dick hot jelly doughnuts filled with the very same jelly he had swung aboard. After the captain had finished an extra cup of coffee, he lighted his pipe and beckoned to Dick. He had noted that Dick was interested in a framed picture of a canal boat hanging inside on the cabin wall.

"Sonny," he began, "I saw you looking at that lithograph of a canal boat in there. Not much like the *Ella E.*, is it? That's the kind of canal boat that quality folks used to really enjoy traveling on. They were called 'packets' and had comfortable staterooms and dining rooms with servants to help. Did you notice the pretty ladies sitting on the top deck with their beaux? How contented they look seated there watching the scenery. No rush! No bustle! No road dust! 'Clinton's Big Ditch,' as Governor Clinton's enemies called it, furnished as clean and genteel a way to travel as ever you'll see. They started digging the canal away back in 1817. Planned to connect

Buffalo, on Lake Erie, with Albany, on the Hudson, by water. They did it, too, by 1825. Cost over seven and a half million dollars. But it's been a great help in the growth and commercial development of the Empire State! Too bad the railroad has put the packets out of business. They looked right pleasing to us canalers.

"The *Seneca Chief*, all dolled up for the holiday, was the first boat to go through. She left Buffalo October 26, 1825. Traveled day and night till November 4th, when she arrived at New York to dump into the Atlantic Ocean the barrel of Lake Erie water she'd fetched from Buffalo.

"When the *Seneca Chief* left Buffalo, cannon began to boom all along the waterway. In less than an hour and a half the signal had reached New York City. Some of the boats in the procession brought along wild animals, birds, and fish. It was a big day for New York State. Many emigrants going West traveled the first stage by Erie canal boat.

"Governor Clinton thought that forty feet was plenty wide enough for a canal in those days. Since then they've widened it to seventy feet at the top and fifty-six feet at the bottom. And there's seven feet of good Lake Erie water in it for many a mile. Near

Rome they get water from the Black River Canal. Below there as far as Syracuse, it's from Cazenovia Lake. The flow is from west to east, for Buffalo is five hundred and sixty-eight feet above water level at Albany."

"But how can you go uphill in a canal boat?" Dick interrupted.

"*Locks* are the answer, my boy," the captain smiled, "and a wonderful old invention they are; as old as civilization itself. You just float your boat into a lock and close the back gate; let in fresh water till you are raised fifteen feet higher; open the front gate and float out at the higher level. Your

horses have walked up the grade on the towpath and are all ready to hitch and pull you along. Wait till you see the great locks at Lockport. Five of them in a stairsteps. And right alongside them five more to take your boat down on the return trip."

Even though Dick had been told about locks, he was amazed when he saw the way one worked. It seemed so easy for the water to lift the heavy boat to a higher level. Sometimes the gatekeeper allowed him to help work the tread that closed the gates. There were numerous locks as they passed up the Mohawk Valley to Schenectady. Sometimes the canal was carved out of the side of a cliff as it ran through a gully. At others it flowed on an aqueduct higher than the surrounding lowlands. After sundown in the great swampy places, Dick heard the pinkeltinks peeping in such numbers that they were almost deafening. Night birds called and frogs croaked.

On the third day, Ned said, "Those smart mules of yours are learning towpath manners very fast. You may ride them this afternoon if you wish."

Dick lost no time after dinner in leading Jack and Jinny over the plank and onto the towpath. Jinny was lead horse, so he climbed on her back. Ned cast off the tie line from the canal stanchion. Dick thumped the sides of the mule with his heels. Both animals were willing to go. They dug their hoofs into the dirt like the good pullers they were. In no time the *Ella E.* was moving. Dick was thrilled as he looked back and saw what he and the mules had done. Then, just to show he was a true canaler, he sat sideways on Jinny's back. This was the way Ned always rode, and Dick wanted to be as much like a regular canaler as possible. He had watched carefully when teams passed on the towpath. Now, as he met one, he was very careful to handle his mules and towline rightly. He had learned that mistakes were not readily forgiven on the towpath. Some of the boats had tough crews and tougher captains. They were ready to fight at the drop of a hat. Tangled towlines riled their tempers, and the greenhorn who was responsible might end with a black eye or a ducking in the canal.

"Good boy!" called Captain Erwin after Dick had successfully passed his third boat. "Looks like you won't be ducked this trip!"

That evening the air was quite balmy, and after supper, when the boat had been tied up for the night, they all carried chairs up on deck. They had stopped at a beautiful spot in the country and the moon was full. So when Ned took out his harmonica and played tunes by Stephen Foster, Ma Erwin and the captain were in the right mood to join in the songs. They sang them well, too, for they had good natural voices.

143

"Old Black Joe," "My Old Kentucky Home," "O Susanna," "Jeanie with the Light Brown Hair," all floated out over the quiet summer landscape. When Gyp, the dog, threatened to lift his own voice in a canine howl, a stern word from the captain quieted him.

Dick was fascinated by the ease with which Ned played his harmonica. When the music was over Dick said, "That looks so easy, Ned. Let me try."

But he found it was not as easy as it looked.

"Come up to the bunks," suggested Ned. "I have a harmonica with a single set of reeds there. It's better for beginners. This one has a double set of reeds. You can use it after you learn on the other."

Ned showed Dick how to "tongue" the harmonica so as to get a tune and a chord with it. Dick played so long at it that Ned finally exclaimed, "Get to bed, kid, or the captain will be after you! We start early tomorrow, you know." So Dick handed back the harmonica and tumbled into his bunk.

Captain Erwin was a born salesman. Some canalboat captains liked to get a full load at Albany and ride right through to Buffalo with it. But Captain Erwin chose to make stops at the smaller places, too. Then he could talk to the merchants. When he left

them he always said, "When you send your order to the warehouse just add 'Ship via the *Ella E.*—Captain Erwin.'" And the merchants usually did as he asked, for they liked his jolly spirits and the funny stories, fresh from the big cities, that he always told them. And each time after he had delivered freight, the captain added the money to the leather pouch in the panel. His "bank" he called it, but it didn't seem a very safe bank to Dick.

As they tied up at Fort Plain one morning, Captain Erwin said, "Come with me, Dick. My friend, Cal Twiggs, runs the store here. And this looks like a crate of candy I'm delivering to him. It's a year's supply, probably. Maybe he'll give you some peppermint sticks or red drops. Ned will bring the rest of the freight on the hand truck." Dick went ashore with the captain and the candy.

Cal Twiggs greeted them heartily as they entered his general store. He was seated at a checkerboard, playing checkers with a white-whiskered opponent. Two other customers looked on. They all dipped their hands frequently into a big cracker barrel. Cal Twiggs did not mind. That was the usual way of getting good will, Dick knew. A store without an open cracker barrel lost much trade.

As the captain had predicted, Cal opened the candy crate after interrupting his checker game. He helped Dick generously to stick candy and the peppery red drops. As he ate his candy, Dick's glance roved about the store. It had everything anyone could want, he thought: oil, lamps, candles, big and little jugs and jars, dishes, pans, food, and clothing of all sorts, and even a showcase of harmonicas and other novelties.

While Captain Erwin collected for his freight, Dick was gazing longingly at the harmonicas. He could tell from the loud guffaws that the captain was telling some of his stories, but Dick was too busy, picking out the kind of harmonica he wanted, to listen.

When the captain and Dick went out the door, the captain, as usual, called out, "Don't forget, Cal. Always ship via the *Ella E.!*"

As they walked to the canal the captain observed, "Remember this, Dick, molasses catches more flies than vinegar does!"

The days passed happily as the *Ella E.* went through Utica, Rome, Syracuse, and Rochester. Three weeks on the boat had made Dick feel like a true canaler. He even began to talk like one. Then

on a sunny morning the captain called out to him, "Come here, Dick! We're nearing Lockport. You must be on deck when we get there!"

Dick rushed forward on the top deck and looked westward. There, rising ahead of them, were the five double locks. They were like stairsteps of water cut out of solid rock. Up and up went the *Ella E.*, four

minutes to each lock. And as she rose, Dick looked across at the other boats going down. Ma Erwin hallooed to a captain's wife on the *Superior*. They were all very friendly, these canalers.

"It's another twenty-five miles into Buffalo," said Captain Erwin. "We'll do most of it today and the rest tomorrow morning. We're in no hurry!"

Dick enjoyed the activity of Buffalo as much as he had that at Albany. After their freight was unloaded, there was a short layover. Then cargo was taken aboard for the return trip. Once more, back on the towpath, Dick was glad to climb on Jinny's back. He loved the calm movement of life along the Erie Canal. And he knew that he had three full weeks of fun ahead of him. He was going to enjoy every minute of the trip—including Ma Erwin's good food and the special raisin cookies she made for him.

Dick counted the locks on the way home. He made chalk marks on his bunk for each lock passed by the *Ella E.* There were seventy-two of them. With Ned's help, he at last played a pretty good tune on the harmonica. On pleasant evenings he fished off the stern, and Ma cooked his catch for breakfast.

A couple of days before they reached Albany, the *Ella E.* tied up for the night near a village. About dusk Dick heard a wagon rattle down to the canal bank. He dropped his fishing line and ran to the shore side to see who it was.

Captain Erwin came on deck as a husky voice called, "Here's a barrel of produce for the Red Swan Inn, further down. They'll pay you freightage."

The stranger unloaded the barrel and hurried off in his wagon before Dick could scamper up the bank.

As the deliveryman left, Captain Erwin said, "Ma, I've seen that man somewhere before. He didn't fool me by keeping his hat pulled down over his eyes!"

"I've seen him, too," chimed in Dick. "But I can't remember where!"

About the same time next evening, they stopped near the Red Swan Inn. It faced the highway which crossed the canal at that point.

"Ned," called the captain, "put that barrel on the hand truck and trundle it up to the inn. I'll go ahead and collect the freightage."

Dick had been riding Jinny on the towpath and had not unhitched the team from the towline. They were nibbling grass along the bank.

In the dim light Dick saw a horseman ride up near the *Ella E.* He hitched his horse to a sapling and walked over the plank to the cabin. Ma Erwin looked up from her sewing to see a red beard partly covered by a handkerchief. The eyes above it gleamed wickedly at Ma as he pointed his pistol at her.

"Keep quiet!" he said, "and you won't be hurt!" He went directly to the wall panel where the captain kept his gold and took out the leather pouch filled with the earnings of the *Ella E.'s* trip. Clutching the full pouch, he dashed ashore.

Then Ma Erwin swung into action. Grabbing the muzzle-loading shotgun that the captain always kept handy for a shot at a stray rabbit, she dashed on deck. Ma banged away at the thief as he mounted his horse. He cried out as the buckshot hit his back. But off he galloped, the bag of gold held in one hand.

Dick heard the noise, saw the gun flash, and knew at once what was happening. As the robber's horse approached Dick, he quickly grabbed his mule's bridle and led the team forward. This tightened the towrope and raised it just enough to trip the robber's galloping horse. The unseated rider went headlong into the canal. The bag of gold he had been holding fell almost at Dick's feet.

Dick picked it up and ran toward the cabin, looking back to see whether the robber would follow him. He need not have worried. The thief had had enough of Ma's shooting. He swam the canal and disappeared in the darkness.

The captain and Ned heard the commotion and hurried back to the boat. On the way Ned grabbed the bridle of the thief's stray horse and brought him along.

"Something funny about this freight!" said the captain, when he heard Dick's story and was assured of Ma's safety. "Ned, open up that barrel! The inn says they never ordered it."

A few whacks from Ned's ax laid the barrel open. It contained a few old bricks and some straw.

"Just a fake shipment to draw me and Ned off

while he robbed my till!" exclaimed the captain. "But he didn't figger on Dick!" he continued, as he slapped Dick's back.

Meantime, the fat innkeeper came trotting down the road to investigate the disturbance. "I know nothing about the freight or the thief," he assured the canalers when he got his breath.

But when Ma Erwin described the robber's red whiskers, the innkeeper raised his eyebrows. Then he examined the thief's horse.

"That's Red Ginnerty's horse, or I'm no judge of horseflesh!" he exploded. "We've long suspected that he wasn't too honest. This makes him a highwayman!"

The innkeeper was also county sheriff. In no time he had a posse searching for Red Ginnerty. The thief was betrayed by the barking of a farm dog. He was in a nearby barn loft, shivering. Most of his clothes were hanging on a rafter as he tried to dry them. The posse forced him to dress and go to jail.

"We'll just stay over a day for the trial," announced Captain Erwin.

Dick never forgot that country courtroom scene. He had to testify to seeing Ginnerty's beard at the cabin window three weeks before, when the voyage started; then as to the appearance of Red with the wagon and barrel. And finally as to what he saw of the holdup on the boat the day before. Red was quickly convicted and imprisoned.

Captain and Ma Erwin were grateful to Dick for saving the profits of six weeks' work on the *Ella E*. They told him so next day, as Ma brought forth some hot apple dumplings, Dick's favorite dessert, and a last treat before they reached Albany.

Shortly after they were tied up at the wharf, Dick's father arrived to take him home and heard all about Dick's adventure with the robber.

"I'm proud of you, Dick!" he commented. "That was fast thinking when you tripped the robber's horse!"

"Yes, and the judge made no disposition of the thief's animal!" rejoined the captain. "We have it right on board. You may as well take it right along with you. If you feed it for a while you can claim it for its board."

Mr. Sefton thought that that sounded sensible and planned to ride the horse home. "Ginger knows Dick well, so he can ride Ginger home," he remarked with a smile.

Ma Erwin stuffed Dick's pockets with cookies after

giving him a hearty hug. Then Ned pulled from his shirt pocket his second-best harmonica.

"You take this home and show your ma and pa how you've learned to play," Ned said generously. Dick was willing enough, for he loved that harmonica.

The captain smiled. He gave Dick a firm handshake. "You're a real canaler now, Dick," he said. "Come next vacation, you ought to be about ready to help out on the *Ella E*. We can use a handy boy like you if your father can spare you."

Dick beamed.

"I guess that's your answer, Captain," said his father.

Ned held Ginger's bit, as Dick climbed on from a stanchion.

Dick talked happily of the trip all the way home.

As they approached the Sefton cottage, Mrs. Sefton came out to greet them. Dick pulled out his harmonica and the horses pranced into the stable yard to the tune of "O Susanna!"

"It's been a wonderful trip!" exlaimed Dick, as he slid off Ginger's back and felt his mother's arms go around his shoulders. "It's sure good to be home, Mom, and next year the captain says I can work all summer on the *Ella E*."

The Flag of France

Let's Visit France

France is the oldest nation in Europe. It is a small country shaped like a shield. Most of the year, it enjoys mild climate. On the fertile lowlands, French farmers grow wheat and other grains, potatoes, sugar beets, vegetables, and olives; they raise horses, cattle, sheep, and goats. On the hills, grapes are grown to make the famous French wines like champagne. Fishing is a big industry and France is rich in coal and iron ore. In the cities, people produce silk and cotton textiles, perfumes, and automobiles. The French are also well known for their laces, fashionable gowns, and fine fabrics. More tourists visit France and the beautiful capital city of Paris than any other place in the world. The French people are independent, full of initiative, and great lovers of art. Many kings have ruled France, but today she is a republic with a parliament and president. The French nation was our ally in the American Revolution as well as in both world wars.

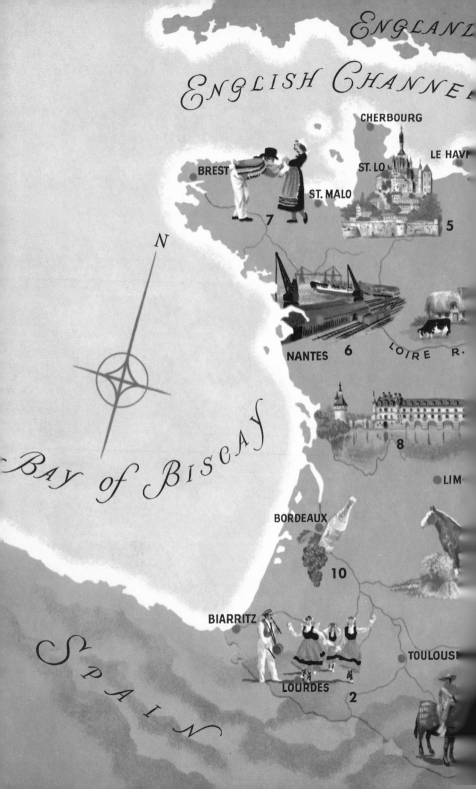

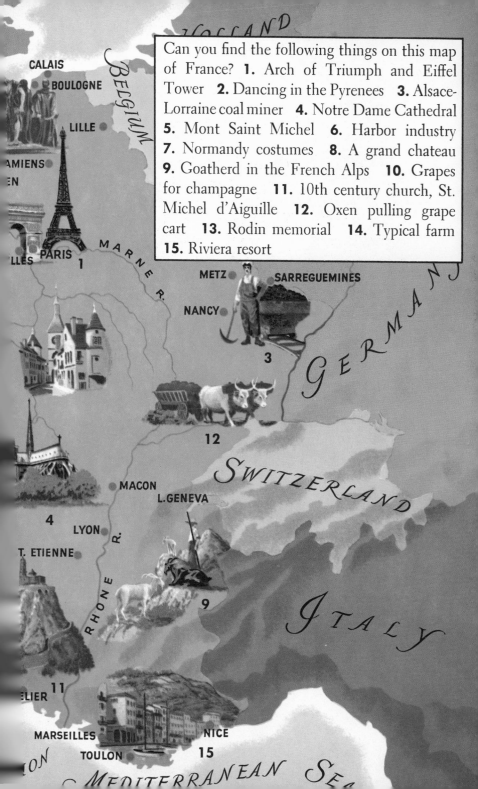

Can you find the following things on this map of France? **1.** Arch of Triumph and Eiffel Tower **2.** Dancing in the Pyrenees **3.** Alsace-Lorraine coal miner **4.** Notre Dame Cathedral **5.** Mont Saint Michel **6.** Harbor industry **7.** Normandy costumes **8.** A grand chateau **9.** Goatherd in the French Alps **10.** Grapes for champagne **11.** 10th century church, St. Michel d'Aiguille **12.** Oxen pulling grape cart **13.** Rodin memorial **14.** Typical farm **15.** Riviera resort

HOLLAND

BELGIUM

CALAIS

BOULOGNE

LILLE

AMIENS

EN

LLES

PARIS

1

MARNE R.

METZ

SARREGUEMINES

NANCY

3

GERMANY

12

SWITZERLAND

MACON

L.GENEVA

4

LYON

RHONE R.

T. ETIENNE

9

ITALY

11

ELIER

MARSEILLES

NICE

TOULON

15

ION

MEDITERRANEAN SEA

At the center of Paris stands the Arch of Triumph, planned by Napoleon. Beneath its arch lies a grave of the Unknown Soldier. The beautiful Cathedral of Notre Dame, below, was built centuries ago on an island in the Seine River.

Printed in the United States of America